The CONFESSIONS of an ALSO-RAN

Dedication

I have no alternative but to dedicate this book to Paul (Phillips).
Otherwise he will sue me for defamation of character.

The
CONFESSIONS
of an
ALSO-RAN

Peter Ashley

Illustrations by
Heather Clarke

FARMING PRESS LTD
Wharfedale Road, Ipswich, Suffolk IP1 4LG

First published 1987

ISBN 0 85236 168 8

British Library Cataloguing in Publication Data

Ashley, Peter
The Confessions of an Also-Ran.
1. Swine——England
I. Title
636,4′0092′4   SF396.G7

ISBN 0-85236-168-8

Phototypeset by Galleon Photosetting, Ipswich
Printed and bound in Great Britain by Redwood Burn Ltd, Trowbridge

BEGINNINGS

SOME YEARS ago I was foolhardy enough to persuade a young friend to give up a good job and to join with me in a new venture. This was to establish a new pig unit on an existing site where urban Middlesex shades into rural Hertfordshire. Paul, whose job, though good, was also full of tension and frustration, greeted the challenge with enthusiasm. Our experiences over the succeeding years, faithfully recorded in *Pig Farming* magazine and now here, illustrate only too well that truth can be quite as strange as fiction. Certainly, because it is real, the truth can be more painful, and sometimes more amusing.

Fortunately, both Paul and I were lucky enough to be born with a sense of humour, and we can usually see the funny side of any happening, however disastrous. At least, we can in retrospect. It is this blessed facility of laughter which more than anything kept us going through seven years of thick and thin – usually thick, like the pile on our bank manager's carpet, which we came to know well.

The chronicling of our inadequacies, our few successes and our frequent failures has proved a useful escape valve. At least, it has for me. I am not sure that Paul has always appreciated his starring role in some of the more bizarre happenings, but he has never complained. Indeed, it has been his amused recollection of many of the incidents in this book which has enabled me to record them accurately.

This account will also, I hope, give solace to other struggling farmers, for whom there is no greater encouragement than to see your neighbour in an even worse pickle than you are yourself. As the Chinese say, in a gale it is comforting to see your neighbour's roof blow off.

Here beginneth . . .

    *Once upon a time Peter and Paul decided to start a new pig enterprise.
They consulted with the Wise Men; or, as they are called in farming
circles, the Wiseacres. They trod the humble path to the Temple of Plenty;
or, as it is sometimes called by hard-up borrowers, the House of Usury.
From the former they received muted encouragement; from the latter, some
of the needy. Paul sold his house. Peter increased his overdraft.*

    *For seven long years they struggled together to create a piggy empire. At
the end of that significant period they decided discretion was the better part
of valour. They packed it in.*

    But it was a lot of fun. . . .

Chapter One

THE PIG enterprise to be described in these pages has no
particular claim to fame. It was not very efficient and certainly
not very profitable. On the two sites it inhabited, most of the
time it looked as though the Augean Stables had a piggy rival.
Such records as were kept were in a tatty school exercise book,
or on scraps of dirty paper torn from meal bags. When transferred by experts into computerised costings they merely
emphasised that we were not doing very well.

The more athletic and adventurous of those of the inmates
who were being fattened up for slaughter periodically staged a
mass breakout into the alleyways, or the meal store, or the
concrete yard – usually when we had just completed a new
strip. On bad days, when the gates had been left open, they
were into the road and away, giving a tyre-screeching shock to
those hurrying commuters using our narrow lane as a short cut.

From the breeding unit of second-hand pre-fabs, converted
from human habitations, the occasional sow headed with a
lumbering canter into the neighbouring wood, having slipped
her tether and/or her young, her quivering rump defiant as it
disappeared among the trees. Tiny piglets, weaned into sup-
posedly safe accommodation, became expert mountaineers.
Their little legs somehow clambered up the steep sides of their
cell using the water-bowl as a support. They then tipped over
the edge and fell with a sickening thud into the slurry below,
miraculously surviving to scamper off at full speed in search of
their mums, and to tell the tale.

Too many of the cantankerous brutes insisted upon dying
before their time, in spite of numerous shots of penicillin, the
veterinary equivalent of sliced bread. This always seemed to

occur at weekends, when our friendly neighbourhood slaughter-house was shut, so there was no possibility of anticipating the demise and at least getting something for the carcase.

A promising farrowing run would come to an abrupt halt when we had a power failure and no stand-by generator. This would usually be at night, well after the last tour of inspection. Or gilts would pretend they were not even pregnant, and then before dawn farrow down in our home-made stalls with disastrous consequences.

When we sold finished pigs to the abattoir they were more often than not either just too light or just too heavy to qualify for top price. Gradings varied from very good to very bad, especially the latter when pigs were plentiful and prices poor. On the unit the pigs consumed an inordinate amount of food, and our food costs were not helped by hundreds of sparrows who twittered gratefully around the mill-and-mixer machine in the food store, and sneered at the ageing moggy.

In other words, the unit which Paul and I set up together proved to be a pretty run-of-the-mill, average sort of unit. It was very much a poor relation to the units featured in such specialist publications as *Pig Farming*, which describe the standards of excellence which can be achieved. For a variety of reasons, not the least of which was our own incompetence, we never managed to approach, even on tiptoe, such fame and fortune.

It all started one day when a farming friend, who had just bought a new farm, asked me what he should do with a 2,000-place pig-fattening unit which came with it, as he knew nothing about pigs himself. He had obviously been impressed by my apparent know-how and affluence, as I had paid his contractor's bills promptly. Rather patronisingly I agreed to go and give it the once-over, and then proffer my expert advice. I little realised what I was letting myself in for.

On a dull, dank day this farm turned out to be a forbidding place. Situated right on top of a hill, it was exposed to all the winds from heaven (and sometimes, we thought later, from hell). The gaunt Victorian farmhouse was surrounded by a dispiriting collection of semi-tumbledown buildings and 140 acres of arable land bulldozed into one large field. Crowning

10

all was 'The Piggery', a vast concrete and asbestos newish building, connected by an umbilical cord to an older, smaller version. It was all approached by a long gravel track, rutted and potholed and, as it turned out, a useful if not very conventional, slurry overflow.

'The Piggery' basically consisted of two fattening houses. These, to my old-fashioned eyes, were the height of modernity. A raised walkway divided two rows of pens, which from one end of the larger house stretched away into the misty distance. The pens had an outside, uncovered slurry channel, with pits to hold the slurry at one end of each building. There was a decent loading/holding/casualty (for us) pen, with a most impressive built-in weighing machine. Having endured agonies over the years siphoning pigs through a single weigher from an inconvenient passage, this set-up had great attractions for me. Unfortunately, we never did get it to work.

In an adjacent barn lurked the even greater pièce de résistance, a large pit, still half-full of putrid meal, flanked by a meal grinder and mixer, and the necessary motors to power a *pipeline feeding system*. Through this, in theory, surged a nutritious liquid along a wide-diameter pipe, the liquid then passing through valves which controlled the supply to each pen. (Practice was something different.) For years I had been exhorted by advisers to install such a system on my own unit, and here was a prototype, ready for use. My earlier reservations about this method of feeding pigs proved, in our case, to have been only too well founded.

The only immediately apparent snag to this high-tech unit was the fact that even on a subsequent visit on a warm day it felt bleak and cold, but I philosophically reflected that when full of pigs it *must* be warm. How wrong I was. Fertiliser bags roughly tacked over the spaced boarding were another hint that perhaps the idea of fresh-air ventilation had been taken to unnecessary extremes, especially as the site was so exposed. Fresh air can be a mixed blessing when it arrives direct from the Arctic. The roof also seemed very high for the purpose of a fattening house. I learned later that the reason for this was to qualify the building as a general-purpose structure, which made it eligible for grant aid.

In addition to the two fattening houses and the adjoining

large barn housing the feed unit, there was also a small, jerry-built structure nearby, roughly converted into a sow/farrowing house. The previous owner had obviously kept pigs in all the other older buildings on the farm but a quick mental calculation suggested that to raise the number to the optimistic two thousand quoted, he must have had them in the farmhouse as well.

However, at this time the situation and the size of the unit were of only academic interest to me. My thoughtful advice, given with the due solemnity befitting an expert, was that the set-up obviously had a lot of potential, though the cost of stocking it would be daunting. It would be a wonderful place for a keen young man to be given a start. My friend scratched his head, looked worried, and said he would think about it. After all, it is quite a shock to be lumbered with a monumental piggery you do not really want, especially if you do not like pigs. 'And there's nothing else I can really use it for, is there?' he said mournfully, as we stood together on the cat-walk, eyeing the double line of empty pens stretching away from us. 'That's the trouble with specialist buildings,' I replied with my new-found authority. 'They are very difficult – and very expensive – to convert.' Indeed, The Piggery would have had to have been completely gutted to put it to another use. We got into our respective vehicles and went, we thought, our separate ways.

Fate was now to take a hand. One evening during harvest, when I was quietly engaged in my normal occupation of minding the machinery and my own business, Paul, dressed as a natty junior executive, arrived on the scene, ostensibly for a chat. Paul was one of a long line of lads whom I had employed over the years to help on my farm at weekends and holiday times.

On this particular evening, as the grain trailers came and went and the machinery rattled away, Paul soon let it be known that he was thoroughly fed up with his job as a junior manager for a large company. Management complacency and union militancy in his depot were making his life a misery. 'Custom and practice are the watchwords,' he said. 'Get any action, or rather, inaction, like a long tea break, established as custom and practice, and you'll have a national strike if you try to alter it.' I listened fascinated, and appreciated the friendly harmony of the farming industry.

'Do you know,' continued Paul, 'we are meant to work a night shift. The only chap who went in was the one who clocked everybody else on and off. Then he got fed up because all his mates were in the pub or doing their second jobs, and they arranged for members of the afternoon and morning shifts to see to the clocking.'

'What about the management?' I asked.

'They keep out of the way.'

'But no firm can go on like that for long,' I said.

'They can,' Paul replied. 'In any case, most of the men want the branch to shut down so they can get their redundancy.' (This happened some years later.)

As it got colder and darker, Paul and I chatted on, waiting for the last load to arrive so I could shut up shop. While I was feeling chilled and depressed by these revelations of the goings-on in the outside world and by Paul's unenviable position, the germ of an idea in the area of my head which passes for brain slowly fructified.

'How about,' I suddenly blurted out, 'taking over a two-thousand-pig unit?'

'Love to,' replied Paul, without a perceptible pause. Oh dear! Little did he or I suspect the consequences of that brief exchange, or the adventure we were to undertake together in a leaky craft in a swirling river of combined whey, meal and slurry, pigs bobbing around in the middle as perpetual hazards, and the navigable channel passing far too near the bank (Lloyds) for comfort.

Paul at this time was in his early twenties and nearly as hirsute as when I had first met him, having merely transferred, in deference to convention, some of his hair from the nape of his neck to his face. He was an active and athletic young man of wide interests and enthusiasms. As readers will soon appreciate, his impulsiveness occasionally got him into difficult situations, though he had enough natural intelligence to correct his mistakes quickly, but not always before they had created a certain amount of chaos. I have mentioned his fortunate capacity for laughter, and over the next few years my wife and I came to admire the cheerful way he accepted one set-back after another.

As it turned out Paul was half-way through his first marriage, to a young lady he had met at college. She followed the twin

13

vocations of dedicated feminism and social work, a fairly common combination it appears. Paul and his wife had been living in a small terraced house in the East End, handy for both their jobs, and which they had modernised themselves. Indeed, we had not long before paid them a visit to celebrate the laying of the last drain. Paul came from a local Hertfordshire family, so transfer back to the country did not come as a culture shock to him. Though I am not at all sure that his wife was that thrilled to have her journey time to work doubled, and to have to move into a cold, isolated country cottage just when they had got their own house habitable.

By that instantaneous acceptance of my proposal, and our subsequent agreement to go ahead, Paul altered the course of his own life and that of his wife; to a lesser extent he altered the course of my life too. By encouraging him to start a new life I was equally responsible for that watershed in our lives. But as I always lecture my own children, with a degree of sanctimoniousness that even I find tedious, if you work hard enough at something it usually turns out best in the end. I think, with hindsight, all involved in the saga of The Piggery and The New Piggery can claim that was true in our case. Though, by God, there were plenty of times when we might have doubted it.

Chapter Two

'If you're going to turn into a pig, my dear,' said Alice seriously, 'I'll have nothing more to do with you. Mind now!' (L. Carroll)

HAVING SOMEWHAT impulsively agreed to walk to the edge of the cliff, all Paul and I had to do now was to clear away the undergrowth, join hands, and jump off. First, we had to convince the owner of The Piggery that we were just the chaps he was looking for to take the burden of a huge, empty unit off his hands. When I tentatively put the proposal to him he responded quite enthusiastically, and said, 'If you and Paul can make a go of it, good luck to you.' I think he was relieved not to have to look further for a solution, but the actual agreement took a deal of working out.

It can be very disadvantageous to a landlord to create any sort of tenancy, particularly an agricultural tenancy, which under present legislation can survive for up to three generations, and will effectively halve the freehold value of a farm. Over the next few months we thrashed out the details of who would be responsible for what, what rent we would pay, and so on. Eventually an agreement was drawn up and signed. I think what really clinched the deal was that I undertook that so long as we were given at least six months' notice we would quit if required.

The main item of this agreement which sticks in my mind is that the owner, and this was where his lack of experience worked in our favour (though to be truthful we were just as ignorant), voluntarily said that he would clear the slurry from the slurry pits. One of his principal reasons for wanting to fill The Piggery was to get slurry for his light-land farm, though I do not think his near neighbours in their trim commuter detacheds were all that thrilled. As it turned out, slurry became one of our main bugbears, and made me appreciate the simplicity

15

of my own deep litter (or, more usually, deep muck) system. Anyone who believes what the salesmen of slurry systems say wants his head examined. Essential training for all slurry experts should be a spell dealing with breakdowns on a working pig farm during the winter. That would quieten them down! Sadly, the occasional fatality from the noxious gases only emphasises how hazardous such systems can prove.

A further propitious circumstance was that we were lucky enough to obtain a cottage for Paul and his wife to rent from a neighbouring farmer. When quite by chance I appealed to him for help, he said that if Paul minded his farmhouse while he and his wife were away on an extended visit to relations in Australia, on their return Paul could have one of the farm cottages which was falling vacant. As with the pig unit I made a similar promise to vacate if required, and I really cannot understand why such undertakings, voluntarily entered into, should not be legally binding – for farms as well.

Though the cottage was some four miles from The Piggery, which was not ideal by any means, especially as it was approached by high-banked lanes which resembled the Cresta Run after snow and/or ice, it was at least good accommodation for the time being. Paul, with youthful enthusiasm, would belt backwards and forwards between cottage and pigs several times a day as though there were no tomorrow, until he received his come-uppance one icy morning when he slid side-on into another vehicle, which effectively slowed him down a bit.

Everything thus seemed to be going our way. We still had some nagging doubts about the unit, which were partially allayed when the previous owner assured me on the phone that he had done very well with it. With hindsight I can well believe this, given the easier times in which he was trading. But in fairness to Paul, I thought we ought to consult the experts. We got two in to look at the site, one of whom confessed to considerable reservations, the other of whom said that it was a splendid unit, especially for producing baconers. This healthy divergence of opinion made it easy to stick to my principle, which is to listen and take note of advice, and then do what *you* think is right. This principle was strongly reinforced for me at one meeting I attended, when, emboldened by free liquor, I asked one of the largest and most successful pig producers in the country how he made investment decisions. 'I just go ahead if I feel it is right,' he replied. It is this instinct for the right decision which is, to me, an essential part of any successful entrepreneurial activity. It explains why most governmental and large organisational decisions get bogged down in expertise, bureaucracy, hierarchical command and sheer ineptitude; and why the decision, when eventually arrived at, is usually the wrong one, and always too late. You will realise as we progress that *my* instinct is not that good.

The other public relations exercise which I felt I ought to do was to prepare some sort of forward analysis for the bank, to justify our request for a large sum of money. Heretically, I consider cash flows, forward budgets, economic analyses and so on just cosmetic procedures, which have little relation to actual performance, past, present or future. In farming we have virtually no control over the end price we receive and there are far too many imponderables: Acts of God, Acts of the French, Acts of the Monetarists (or non-Monetarists), illegal Acts by our EEC partners (the French mainly), non-Acts (strikes), subsidies paid by the French (among others) to their wine-swilling, garlic-eating, inefficient peasant farmers, interference by the French (among others) with free trade, and the dumping of British lamb and beef in the middle of the highway.

However, I was quite prepared to swim with the tide if required, though I had learnt my lesson long before, when I was contemplating putting up a broiler chicken unit. We complied with every conceivable economic analysis requirement, took all the advice available, and based all our forecasts upon an expected return of at least one shilling and ninepence (old money) per pound of chicken, which was the *lowest* return my potential associates had ever received. Quite reasonable, you may think – until I tell you that the *highest* return I ever received was one shilling and sevenpence halfpenny.

Similarly with The Piggery. When we started and did our costings the main ingredient of our feed, barley, was about £77 a ton. Over the intervening years this has swung between that figure and a high of about £130. Our 'other costs' – electricity, water, etc. – have trebled. Our sale price, apart from one or two halcyon periods, has remained obstinately low. All this illustrates just how wayward any forward budget can be.

17

However, certain people feel easier if you produce some sort of a forecast, so we did. At least it convinces them that you can write and add, and that you are not one of those unfortunates who feature in social enquiry reports and who cannot even understand a railway timetable or add up their check-out in a supermarket. This conveniently ignores the fact that most of us find difficulty doing either of these.

The kindest adjective I can find for my original analysis is 'euphoric'.

We decided for reasons I cannot quite recall to form a limited liability company. I suppose that was in case we went broke, though the bank insisted upon personal guarantees. We discovered an interesting fact, that there are people who actually make a living by forming companies, and then selling them to clients like us, who wish to avoid delay in getting a name approved and so on. It can be most frustrating to find that the name you have so carefully selected is already being used. For a hundred pounds we bought a company with quite a nice name, and a sufficiently broad definition of functions to include pig farming. Our main claim to fame must be that we probably had the most highly qualified shareholders of any pig company. Between the three of us (Paul, his wife, and myself), we had university degrees in chemical engineering, sociology and history. This fact, together with my earlier reference to the number of illiterates and innumerates, raises the interesting question as to just how well our educational system is actually functioning.

So, since that harvest meeting we had done quite a lot. Paul had given in his notice, to be tantalisingly offered both promotion and a move to less union-dominated pastures (Hong Kong!), had put his house up for sale to raise capital, and had found somewhere else to live, albeit as a tenant. We had signed an agreement for our new unit, and formed a company to run it. We had money from the bank. They had offered us twice our own stake of twelve thousand pounds, which was a lot of money a decade ago. To be truthful, I think this was because they knew I was credit-worthy, as I owned my own farm. It is a reflection upon the role of banks in our society that I am convinced that new entrants, however competent, would never be able to negotiate anything like that sort of a deal. More's the pity.

We had a starting date, January 1st, though our landlord kindly agreed to let us take possession earlier if we wished. Our commitment, especially Paul's, was total, and almost matched our optimism. All we now had to do was to introduce some stock into the empty, echoing, draughty expanse of The Piggery, and hope that they would thrive, and we would prosper. With some trepidation we wrote out a cheque for the first quarter's rent, and set about buying some weaners to start off our fattening enterprise.

We arranged to buy these from two sources. My existing partner in a breeding unit in Suffolk, although already really fully committed to another buyer, promised us a load or two to get us going, and undertook to expand his herd slightly to help us. A local pig buying and selling group, who later became so dynamic and thrusting that they disappeared right up the spout with some three thousand five hundred pounds of my money, put us in touch with another supplier.

As it turned out, this supplier had just the right type of pig for our new enterprise, whereas those from my Suffolk partner were really only suitable for heavy hogs, as they stuffed themselves silly with short-bodied glee towards the anonymity of pork pies and sausages. We had decided to concentrate on producing porkers and cutters in The Piggery, mainly for a quick turnover and some cash flow. For the pork market it is essential to produce a lean, meaty pig. To add a spice of extra excitement to our first Christmas in partnership together, we arranged for our first load of weaners to be delivered on December 21st. 'May as well start as soon as we can,' said Paul with understandable enthusiasm.

Before then, we had to master the complicated array of knobs and buttons which in theory controlled the various motors of the feeding system, which it was essential to get functioning correctly. I must here admit that I never did learn how to work the set-up, and I spent a lot of my praying time beseeching the Good Lord to keep Paul healthy and at work.

Paul had an interesting and instructive, not to mention filthy introduction to the joys of self-employment on a pig farm, when for a start he had to replace a bearing in the bottom end of the auger in the wet meal pit. We found to our dismay that this pit had also been used for swill. Even a thorough cleansing of the pit of the putrid meal and bewhiskered swill lurking there failed to remove that frightful rancid smell, or that slimy feel. This, combined with rust and old grease plus the stubborn refusal of the shaft to release the broken bearing, became a stern test of temperament and endurance, which I failed almost immediately. Fortunately, Paul was made of sterner stuff, and possessed the phlegmatic disposition essential for competent mechanics.

When the repair was eventually completed we were able for the first time to pump clean water round the system, only to find that every valve was jammed solid, and had to be carefully freed. The use of too much force either wrenched the tap from the housing, or cracked the pipe joint. The sense of triumph as we not only succeeded in getting water to gush into each trough, but managed to stop the flow to order, waned progressively as a tired Paul approached the twenty-sixth valve. But at long last the whole system throughout the two fattening houses was working after a fashion, though only at the very moment when the lorry arrived with our first 180 pigs.

The driver, particularly interested because he had known the farm in its heyday, backed up to the unloading bay, and the pigs tumbled off the lorry, released at long last from their swaying, claustrophobic transporter. They wandered bemusedly down the long alleyway to their new quarters, which they investigated, rightly, with some suspicion. With their arrival at The Piggery, empty for too long, our enterprise acquired a meaning and direction lacking until then. 'Good to see the place going again,' remarked the driver. 'Last time I was here was just before they had swine vesicular disease for the second time.' That we had not known. It did nothing to boost our confidence or improve our Christmas spirit.

Although this first winter was a mild one, the introduction of what were to us enormous numbers of pigs into the cavernous voids of The Piggery had little effect on the ambient temperature, and these early arrivals spent most of their time huddled in the sleeping areas on top of one another. It was quite fascinating to see them uncurl themselves at feeding time, legs, ears, tails, testicles and heads appearing from the most unlikely places; or screaming for food, with that high-pitched banshee wail which carried on pulsating sound waves from the top of the hill to all the neighbouring villages. It started dogs howling, sent housewives running to the door and drove nervous toddlers beneath the secure haven of their cot blankets. The local Calvinist minister, until he got used to it, was convinced the end of the world was nigh.

The trouble was that as soon as Paul started the mixer, all the pigs knew that grub was nearly up and started yelling for it. Unfortunately, there was inevitably a delay while water, whey and meal churned around to the correct consistency, then a further delay as Paul sprinted along the walkways opening each valve in turn for a set time. Mind you, by the time you got towards the end of the line, the cacophony of noise had so numbed your senses that all self-discipline disappeared, and you shot the meal in anyhow, just to shut the noisy brutes up.

It was especially annoying when a particular valve stubbornly refused to open. Paul would abandon it and leave it to the end, but by then the pigs in that pen, who well knew that their turn had come and gone, would be going absolutely berserk, foaming at the mouth, clambering frenziedly over each other and in and out of the trough, and using the most foul porcine language.

Feeding time thus resembled an obstacle race, accompanied by the sort of noise which drove poor Devon Loch (the Grand National runner) to attempt the splits with fame and a jubilant Queen Mother only a few short strides away.

Paul was pretty agile, and he had to be to dart along the first walkway, then over one six-foot wall, across an intervening space, up another six-foot wall, tiptoe along the back edge of a pen to reach the second walkway, and then down sixty yards or so of often slippery timber, with a pen every few yards. Even his balance failed him at times, and he would disappear from view with a dreadful curse. I would see a disconcerted figure emerge from a ruck of pigs, rather like a man with the ball in American football, usually covered in sloshy meal, and often something worse.

Whenever I was present at feeding time at The Piggery I could only be thankful that I had resisted the blandishments of those advisers who had recommended pipeline feeding for my own unit as a necessary alternative to my crude, ad-lib dry meal system, and that I had ignored the warnings that I would never survive in an age in which only the super-efficient high-performer stood a chance. Stubbornly, I maintained that I could not

21

afford the capital outlay, that either improved breeding or improved feed (or both) should prevent pigs going over-fat on ad-lib feeding, as I was constantly told would inevitably happen. In this matter at least I think I can claim to have been proved correct. The ease and lack of stress to man and beast was worth quite a bit to me and I would accept a marginally poorer food conversion. Finally, I *liked* my system, whatever its disadvantages.

The opportunity to find out if I had, as I secretly suspected, been foolishly obstructive to innovation all those years had been too great to resist when The Piggery had loomed (quite literally) on the horizon, complete with its pipeline system. And, after all, Paul was going to do all the work. But the stress at each feed was horrific, not only for Paul, but also for the fighting, slobbering pigs. As soon as the meal gushed from the pipe into the trough, the strongest of the inmates of the pen would be waiting, mouths agape. Having swallowed the first succulent mouthfuls, they then shunted backwards, sprinted to the part of the trough the meal had by now reached, knocked flying any weaker brethren attempting sustenance, took another two or three rapid gulps, then repeated the manoeuvre.

When they reached the end of the trough and could go no further they lay down in it, and let the wet meal flow in through their open jaws, around and under their bodies. When thoroughly wet they stood up and shook this lovely grub all over the floor, then spitefully urinated in the trough. By the time their greed was satisfied the poor old no-hopers were left with little but the smell and their own raging hunger.

Sometimes Paul would start this twice-daily so-called routine, only to find that pressure in the pipe had dropped, and it took an age to feed even one pen. The first time this happened he found when he got to the end of the line of pens that the very last valve was already open – vandals, poltergeists, brain-of-Britain pigs? – and that meal had been gushing happily into the trough, over the floor, down the alleyway, under the door and into the slurry pit. In future, he knew what to look for, but it still took an age to locate the culprit valve, and by then a lot of precious meal would have gone to waste, and the roof would have been raised several inches by the combined frustrated screaming of eight hundred pigs. Pigs in the last few pens to be fed also produced a command performance if Paul misjudged the necessary amount of food, and had to return to the mixer to prepare extra. A throbbing mass of heads would strain upwards towards the walkway and their non-productive valves. Mouths agape, jaws slobbering, they yelled their impatience. If pigs ever get sore throats, ours certainly did not.

Another major snag to our trough feeding was getting the number right in each pen. Too many, and in a week or so a nice even bunch of stores became a heterogeneous mixture of all shapes and sizes; too few encouraged the meal-bathers and trough-foulers. Moreover, even our pigs grew, sometimes quite fast, and if we got the number right to start with, in no time at all it was wrong. What could you do then but wait until the largest were big enough to sell to relieve congestion? But, ah but, they were the greediest, quickest growers. They consistently had far more than their fair share. They rewarded you for this unintended generosity by being nice and fat, and getting down-graded. When the return from the abattoir arrived, you felt that electrocution was *much* too good for them.

Chapter Three

'I can tell you right now that isn't going to work.' (J. Thurber)

IN MY old-fashioned way I could reflect with mixed feelings of satisfaction that my reservations about pipeline feeding had been justified – at least, so far as the fairly primitive system at The Piggery was concerned. I was only grateful that it was Paul and not I who had to cope with it – which he did with admirable equanimity and patience. Fortunately, he had never known anything better.

Another technical innovation which many advisers considered essential to successful pig-keeping, and which I had also resisted for years, was the slurry system of dealing with effluent. The disposal of effluent from stock is a continuing and constant worry for farmers, particularly on farms near built-up areas. The slurry system had been developed as a potential solution, but has probably created as many problems as it has solved, not least the dreadful stench when the slurry is spread. It always seems that the wind perversely shifts direction and it refuses to rain for days whenever slurry is spread within sniffing distance of understandably disgruntled neighbours. Here again, at The Piggery we inherited a system of sorts, and after only a few short weeks there we became all too familiar with the problems associated with slurry – at least on our unit.

For one thing, it is quite amazing how quickly it becomes embarrassing. When the pit is full, you *have* to get rid of the wretched stuff. But the ground is too wet; the machine breaks down; the neighbours complain. Still the pigs, oblivious to such problems, continue to urinate and defecate copiously. Rain-water continues to seep into the pit from the sodden ground to aggravate the situation.

Moreover, our landlord had taken on far more than either he wished, or was able to cope with. At the crucial times his men were otherwise gainfully employed, or on holiday or, if they got wind of what was afoot – which was not difficult – AWOL (absent without leave). The slurry tanker he had bought at considerable expense proved a white (or chocolate-coloured) elephant. It only had to be towed from the nettles to respond with a dramatic and ill-timed breakdown.

The two slurry pits on the unit were both inadequate and badly sited. They collected not only slurry but water from heaven, and, if they strayed too near, children from the local primary school and dogs from the nearby housing estate, both groups given far too much freedom. (Thank the Lord they could usually swim.) Once full, these pits overflowed in a most spiteful way. The slimy, foul-smelling liquid slid between the buildings, across the corner of a protesting field, and straight onto the rutted track to the farm, its progress charted by a black channel which resembled the approach of an elongated pre-historic monster.

Once on the comparative haven of the gravel drive, this monster continued sluggishly towards the public road some half-mile distant, slowly losing impetus and, fortunately, part of its consistency to the adjoining fields and, more disconcertingly, to the wheels of passing vehicles. From there it spread to the neighbouring roads, villages and towns.

I once got out of my car in the middle of our local town to visit my bank manager. I then realised with mounting shame that not only I, having trod through the stuff, but my car, having been driven through it, smelt as though The Piggery had arrived in the High Street – as indeed it had, albeit by proxy. I hurriedly retreated to the sanctuary of my own farm, avoiding the glances of incredulity and distaste from side-stepping passers-by as I drove away. I tried to pretend that the muni-cipal drains must have overflowed, and that I was merely from the Ministry of the Environment making a spot check. At home, I phoned my long-suffering bank manager, and told him I had been unavoidably delayed helping to move pigs, which I suppose was true in a way.

We became so annoyed and worried by this slurry problem that Paul eventually volunteered to clear it away when our landlord's workforce was too busy. Our landlord, a pleasant but happy-go-lucky character to whom overflowing slurry was a

non-existent problem until his wife drove her new car through it, cheerfully accepted this foolish offer. As a result, Paul more often than not found himself with this extra chore, which not only knocked the back end out of his ancient tractor, but took up an inordinate amount of his valuable time.

In the end, we decided that enough goodwill was enough, and started charging for this service by deducting an agreed amount from our quarterly rent cheque. We considered this would be the best way of ensuring ourselves prompt payment, as we had experienced the probable delays caused by our landlord's somewhat casual book-keeping methods, which, like those of many farmers, seemed to consist of paying in cheques immediately, and putting everything else behind the clock or under the cartridges on the desk. At the same time this device got us into the most almighty confusion over that tiresome tax, VAT, which it seemed to me we spent our time charging to ourselves, and then reclaiming from the authorities.

I dare not confess to the semi-legitimate subterfuges I was forced to adopt (in case a VAT inspector with a farming background happens to be given this in his Christmas stocking) to avoid the complication of paying this tax, then reclaiming it, then charging it, then reclaiming it in a different name, then trying to apportion the one relevant invoice between two VAT-registered companies, and so on and so on.

Our landlord's insouciance regarding our slurry problem did receive a nasty dent one day when upon the scene arrived one of those beings from outer space, in this case, a lady person, from the Water Board. (Almost as powerful as the VATman.) She had received a complaint, she said, that certain obnoxious substances were being discharged via adjoining fields into a neighbouring watercourse. It had got to stop, she demanded, with some authority, or we would be hung, drawn and quartered. Outraged innocence responded firstly by blaming us (which I should have done in his case) for something of which, of course, he had no knowledge whatsoever. He then promised faithfully that he would make sure the pollution – if such it was and personally he doubted if there was a problem at all – never happened again.

The subsequent course of action taken by the one was to dig a channel to divert the slurry into a convenient bomb crater; by the other, who was obviously not so naive as she appeared, to threaten to send a bill for the pressure hosing of her car, which she had driven inadvertently through the outpourings of a swollen slurry pit.

Unfortunately, but not surprisingly, our slurry pits refused to act on the sensible and scientific principle of the septic tank. If only the solids had sunk to the bottom, allowing a fairly clear liquid to be siphoned off the top, it would not have been too bad. But either the constant filling, or, as I firmly believe, the sporting activities of little gremlins playing slurry polo, kept the consistency that of thin treacle without the sweetness.

Another dodge of our landlord when the slurry problem became too pressing for us all was to build a wall of straw bales around the edge of the pits. Hopefully, they would hold more slurry and put off the evil day. This worked fine as far as it went, but eventually the weight of the slurry became too much even for the saturated bales. They gave way in a spectacular collapse, letting a wall of slurry descend in a miniature avalanche

27

towards the driveway. Two unsuspecting horse-riders, whose mounts shied in terror at the advancing brown flood, bolted back whence they had come, carrying tidings of alarm and sorrow to their trendy riding school.

This time the path of the slurry resembled the progress of an erupting volcano. Fortunately, its pace was fairly rapid, not like the usual trickle, and most of the overflow shot straight over the lane, rather than settling in the ruts and heading for the main road. As the flood subsided, we prayed for rain. That is, when we were not praying that the water-person would not choose this inconvenient moment to arrive on the scene. The bomb crater had long since proved inadequate either as a receptacle or a filter, and was as brimful and as unsavoury as the parent pits it was designed to relieve.

We realised fairly soon that feeding wet meal only made the slurry problem worse by producing even more liquid, but by then we were committed to both systems.

Having got the mix, pump, flow and slosh-into-the-troughs routine working more or less to our satisfaction, and to the partial contentment of the inmates of our closed (we hoped) prison for swinish recidivists, we felt it was time we undertook some research into such mysteries as diets and behaviour patterns. We were becoming uncomfortably aware that our pigs were not really performing as well as they should.

I never ceased to be amazed at the way in which our learned academics occupy their time and spend our money. With incredulity I read a report on the research into a 'deviant' (piggy) behaviour called 'persistent inguinal nose-thrusting', PINT for short. Truly! These researchers solemnly (I assumed the whole thing was not a joke) observed this behaviour in pigs. But why, I wondered, did they consider it deviant, when it is pretty widespread (at least among our pigs) and, therefore, presumably normal?

They came up with the earth-shattering conclusions that 'it is generally the dominant pigs who are the thrusters', and 'the pig being nosed does not have any evolved response'. Well, well, well! I think I could have told them that for a small fee. As Paul sensibly remarked, 'I quite like to see it. It shows the pigs are getting fond of one another.' This is quite important given their aggressive instincts.

28

We also studied with interest the pale, soft, exudative (PSE) meat syndrome, particularly prevalent, we read, in 'stress-prone pigs'. I invented 'SPP' as an abbreviation for this, and claim a patent. This condition (they had not discovered 'syndrome' when I went to school) as all my clued-up readers will know, is what can happen to a carcase if a pig is badly treated on the way to slaughter. I did know something about this, and to prevent stress I have always insisted that my pigs are loaded early in the morning, not mixed with others or even taken to other farms, driven straight to the factory, and killed the same day. I am convinced that to omit any of these can be very costly, besides giving the poor brutes an unhappy end to their brief existence.

Paul and I felt there was plenty of scope for in-depth research at The Piggery. I have described how difficult it was to get the numbers in the pens just right for non-competitive, non-wasteful trough feeding from our meal-gusher system. Numbers were also crucial for communal warmth in the winter, cool comfort in the summer, and the amount the inmates used their sleeping quarters as a lavatory, or their feeding or dunging area as a dormitory.

There are, I am sure, clever chaps (though I doubt if they work in universities) who not only get the balance right, but persuade their pigs that cleanliness is next to Godliness. Human beings do not really enjoy shovelling out caked dung from a cramped sleeping area with little headroom, when they should be mechanically squeegeeing liquid manure easily from the right place to the slurry pit. In our case, about one in three pens behaved, the others had read George Orwell, and were not having any of that sort of co-operation.

If we put straw in the sleeping area they made it wet, then shivered on it. If they kept the dormitory dry, they pushed their weaker mates out of the way and into the cold of the feeding area. These poor despised animals responded by contracting dysentery and squitting into the food trough. There was really no rhyme or reason to it. One lot in one pen were sensible, clean-living, decent sorts of animals, who slept, ate, and dunged all in the right place, watched *EastEnders* at night, and went happily to slaughter, lean and fit.

The next intake, *in the same pen*, were like the worst type of football hooligan, urinated everywhere, killed or maimed each other at the slightest provocation, wore bovver boots at meal-times, slept rough, and made the dung passage a no-go area. They suffered from every ailment in the *TV Vet*'s book, plus a few he had not even heard of. They were, in short, the type of animal which made us wish we were anywhere but in their begrimed, foul-mouthed company.

To give Paul his due, he never complained though, as with all new businesses, the initial euphoria soon wore off, to be replaced by the more mundane necessity of making money, which does not necessarily follow enthusiasm and hard work. Perhaps our biggest mistake was for Paul to start something as big as this with very little experience. After all, looking after my own rather slapdash unit in school and university holidays was hardly adequate preparation for the enterprise we had now undertaken. Ideally, of course, Paul should have had a year or two on other, well-run pig units.

Errors of judgement were at first masked by good trading conditions, but over the following years we have had to buy our experience painfully. It is particularly frustrating to describe the symptoms of some new (to us) disaster to someone like my Suffolk partner Derek, who has seen it all before, recognises the trouble immediately, and then remarks, 'I always give an injection a month before farrowing to prevent that.' If only we had known! Still, it is impossible to anticipate all, which would make life most unexciting. In any case, it is usually the un-expected which occurs. At least, it did on our unit.

Chapter Four

'For buying or selling of pig in a poke.' (T. Tusser)

ONE RESULT of Paul's own in-depth research into the intricacies of diet, was that he introduced a new ingredient into our ration at The Piggery. A persuasive salesman, plus its apparently competitive price – though I must admit I at least never really understood how you compare the price of a liquid with that of a solid – determined Paul to try feeding whey, which was then readily available.

An important reason for this decision was that our second-hand mill-and-mixer unit was obviously going to have trouble coping with future demand. We had bought this outfit at a farm sale. Both Paul and I were nervous and unused to the subtleties of this type of function, and found it hard to follow the staccato utterances of the auctioneer as he moved from tatty lot to rusty heap, accompanied by a jostling group of winking, nodding, stick-poking farmers and dealers. In their tattered layers of clothing, their greasy caps or trilbys, and their muddy boots, they all looked as though they were in the last stages of destitution – until, that is, you saw them in the bar or driving home with their purchases.

Eventually the auctioneer stationed himself by the mill-and-mixer which we hoped to buy, assured by the owner that it was 'as good as new', 'working yesterday', etc. I can only report Paul's subsequent behaviour as what the ad-men call 'impulse buying'. The auctioneer asked for a bid. As always there was a complete silence. He suggested a figure, lowered it, pleaded in a pathetic voice for *any* bid to start with. Nobody made a move or uttered a sound. Individuals looked completely disinterested and concerned with their deep innermost thoughts. I began to think we might get the mill for the proverbial song. I was just plucking up courage to squeak 'fifty pounds', when a voice from

31

beside me in a stentorian tenor shouted, 'two hundred pounds'. It was Paul. It was the one and only bid.

Everybody appeared so flabbergasted at his presumption that before you could say 'Martin Markham' it was knocked down to us.

'Whatever made you say that?' I demanded in utter astonishment.

'I don't know,' said Paul. 'It just came out.'

'Thank God you didn't say two thousand,' I said, and left it at that. It was, after all, the price we had decided would be reasonable, and perhaps (perhaps?) Paul's initiative had unnerved other potential buyers. Apart from a tendency to surround itself with a cloud of swirling dust, this mill-and-mixer served us faithfully all our seven years together, and still grinds and mixes happily on my own farm. I think we can claim it as one of our successes.

However, it was not really big enough for the demands of some eight hundred pigs, particularly as we could not easily store meal, and had to wait for the wet pit to empty before we could unload another mix into it and restart the grinder. And you know what effect that had on the pigs waiting to be fed! So the possibility of using a proportion of whey in the ration which could be pumped in direct was attractive.

To get a supply we had first to hire a storage tank. A few days later this arrived, a huge black cylinder squatting obscenely atop a small and timid lorry, which had somehow transported its burden a hundred miles. We had hired a mobile crane to unload this monster. Unfortunately the crane was not really man enough for the job, and only with the very greatest effort and after several attempts did it manage to lift the tank a few painful inches from the floor of the lorry. The tank then took control. Festooned in ropes and chains it swayed slowly from side to side, having a deliberate look around to sum up the situation. Meanwhile, the crane teetered about, the tank suspended precariously in front, rather like a drunk trying to make it home with a barrel of beer.

As a prelude the whey tank, with one lazy, powerful side-swipe, completely demolished a flimsy lean-to on the side of the barn, then swung slowly and majestically through an arc of 180 degrees, lifting the rear wheels of the crane off the ground as it did so, and threatening to destroy a diesel tank which nestled coyly on the other side of the barn door, and to which it had obviously taken a violent dislike. This was too much for the crane driver, who panicked, and dropped the whey tank on the ground with an almighty clatter, proving at any rate that the concrete floor had been well laid, and that the tank had been built to withstand a siege.

The combined efforts of some six people, crowbars, chains and two tractors eventually coaxed this stubborn brute into the barn, where it settled quite happily, looking just like a submarine in dry dock. Indeed, when Paul emerged from the conning tower in the top after a periodical clean, he could quite easily have been Jack Hawkins surfacing to survey the enemy position.

We were only glad that we had decided to put it on the floor of the barn, rather than on a stand outside. I am sure it appreciated being under cover, as I also suspect it would have deliberately rolled off any perch, probably straight through the farmhouse and into the next parish. It was that sort of an object.

This tank was soon connected to the rest of the hurdy-gurdy of our feed unit and, apart from becoming empty at inconvenient times like Bank Holidays, gave us no further trouble until we came to remove it.

Unfortunately, what nobody had told us was that while whey was jolly good grub, it had one big drawback. Every so often one of our pigs would unexpectedly lie on its back, put its little trotters in the air, and give up the ghost. It was, so our vet lugubriously informed us – I think he had been watching *All Creatures Great and Small* – something called 'whey bloat'. And there was very little we could do about it. Nothing, in fact, apart from stop feeding whey of course. As it was always one of the best pigs which died, we were never that thrilled. But at least it gave us an excuse for unexplained deaths, and 'whey bloat, I'm afraid' covered a multitude of disasters from then on.

Whey in the ration certainly made it a more palatable and sweeter-smelling mixture, and to compensate for the occasional death our pigs did respond with a slightly better growth rate and improved food conversion. But our performance was still way below that of that God-like 'Top Third', so admired by

33

analysts. It was hard enough for us to attain the giddy heights of 'Average'. Undoubtedly, one of our major problems was that of ventilation.

This became all too obvious in our second year when a very hot summer was followed by an unusually severe winter. Even though the roof was high and there were vents in the ridge and Yorkshire boarding along half one side, there was still insufficient air movement in hot weather. We tried removing some of the side asbestos sheets, which made little difference. Finally, in desperation, Paul climbed on to the roof and took off several of the ridge sheets. This did have some effect, but earned us a very old-fashioned look from our landlord, especially as one of the sheets had slid down the roof and smashed on the concrete. However, he confined himself to the hope that we would make sure we replaced them eventually.

I had suggested removing these ridge sheets following an earlier experience on my own farm. I had not realised that years of exposure to the acidic, ammonia-laden vapours arising in a humid cloud from my overstocked pig yards had completely rusted through all the bolts holding the asbestos onto the roof trusses — so much for modern galvanising. A violent gale one night ripped off a section of roof, depositing many broken and mutilated sheets upon my beloved lawn some thirty yards away. It proved a terrible job replacing these in high winds and lashing rain, with hundreds of frenzied pigs galloping around at the foot of the ladders, alternately trying to climb up to join us in the dizzy heights, or giving the bottoms of the ladders a heart-stopping nudge; while the man on the roof outside struggled to keep his position on the slippery surface as his frozen fingers attempted to tighten the nuts. (He was later awarded the Porcine Cross for bravery in the face of the enemy.) All enough to give a safety officer a fit, but just one of the many unscheduled jobs we so-called feather-bedded farmers seem to get all too often.

Eventually, we were one ridge sheet short. This we never replaced, as the hole in the roof proved a very effective ventilation chimney, yet let in surprisingly little rain or snow. So we thought we would try something similar at The Piggery. It did make a marginal difference — but what we really needed was a ruddy great fan at either end.

34

Meanwhile, the pigs sweated and swore, fought and tried with adolescent zeal to fornicate (or worse), defecated everywhere, slept in the trough, and made determined forays into the outside dunging passage (where it was wet and cool) whenever Paul left the connecting door open for a moment. Not unnaturally, growth rate and food conversion figures began to slide off the graph once again.

Having done our best to improve living conditions for the summer we had now to prepare for the colder weather. We had already learned that the sleeping areas really required covers to make them warm and cosy in cold weather, so Paul spent a lot of time in the autumn making temporary shelters (remember, it was not our building) from any second-hand materials we could beg, borrow or steal from the builder's yard of my accommodating brothers-in-law. As a result, when viewed from the ramp, The Piggery resembled more and more a primitive native village; and certainly when the wind blew from the direction of the bubbling, overflowing slurry pits, it smelt as though it had been built upon a malodorous swamp.

These covers were quite effective so far as they went, but being of a jerry-built nature they had the usual disadvantages of such structures. Nor were the pens they covered inhabited by decent law-abiding citizens, but by inquisitive and mischievous miscreants. Any hanging piece of sack, string, plastic, or straw was instantly seized upon by the inmates below decks and, as is their wont, worked at furiously and with great glee until everything started to disintegrate. In no time at all, their insulated ceiling, constructed for their own good, would collapse upon them with a rattle and crunching of corrugated iron, broken asbestos and supporting timbers. I hesitate to criticise Paul, because he always had to labour under great difficulties, but he really was an inspired graduate of Heath Robinson when he set his mind to it.

Paul would arrive next morning to find at least one pen of pigs smothered in dust and straw and sleeping higgledy-piggledy among the debris with satisfied smiles on their faces. Miraculously, and in spite of the nocturnal panic which must have occurred, none perished in these miniature earthquakes, which was even more surprising as our pigs occupied a great deal of their leisure time trying to commit suicide (to spite us), or feverishly spreading disease among themselves.

From the human point of view, these flimsy covers were a snare and a delusion. For they gave an unmerited appearance of solidity, and it was tempting to use them as a walkway when viewing the pens, or sprinting from one side of the building to another. This was disastrous, and inevitably resulted in at least one leg disappearing through the cover, more often than not being followed by the other and then the upper body, which crashed among the startled pigs below to their woofing delight at the humiliation of their human servitor. You could almost hear them saying, 'That'll teach him to keep us waiting for our grub.'

It really is, looking back on it, quite amazing that we have survived to tell the tale.

Chapter Five

'The question is,' said Humpty Dumpty, 'which is to be Master – that's all.'
(L. Carroll)

AFTER A YEAR or so at The Piggery, we were forced to accept that even with the best will in the world Paul could no longer cope single-handed, especially if we were to expand into breeding, as we planned. So far Paul had just about managed on his own.

When, in spite of my impassioned pleading to be careful, Paul had the temerity to put out his shoulder playing rugby, I whipped him out of the casualty department as soon as he was strapped up, so he could come and supervise the pig operation, as opposed to his own. Fortunately, his injury was not serious, but it certainly put the wind up me and his wife, who had to abandon temporarily her own deprived and disturbed human caseload – with whom I must admit to having very little sympathy – to help cope with our hungry pigs, with whom I had every sympathy. I could quite see the point in keeping *them* happy and balanced, off the dope, and away from delinquency and suicidal tendencies.

From time to time he also had help from various friends and relations, anxious for a jolly day in the country. The combination of slosh, slurry and smell proved a regular eye-opener to one or two of the well-meaning ones, who fled hurriedly back to urban normality and never appeared again. But several stuck it out and gave us a great deal of welcome and cheerful support.

One of these was an ex-school chum of Paul, who had progressed through later life via the Young Farmers' Club – which as so often happens provided him with both a wife and an unrequited love of farming – eventually becoming a successful publican. Success in that business usually means that you spend most of your life not only in a swirling cloud of fumes

alcoholic and narcotic, but constantly tempted to 'have one on me'. No wonder publicans have a low life expectancy.

So Alan was only too glad to escape into the relatively fresh air surrounding The Piggery and undertake a slice of hard work. I must admit to some qualms as to what harm we might be doing him when I saw his normally unhealthy pallor take on an even deeper greyish hue, and heard him wheeze throatily as he painfully bent his back. But Paul and Alan merely laughed, and maintained it 'was good for him'. In my experience, things which are 'good for you' are quite often fatal.

These two friends enjoyed the same sense of humour, which has been the saving grace preventing Paul from going completely round the twist, and they could always see the funny side of any minor disaster, like the occasional breakout into the alleyways or the outside passage into which the dung was scraped from the pens. Inevitably, two or more pens of pigs would get themselves well and truly mixed, as well as completely exhausted, galloping with woofs of delight up and down the hundred yards or so of slithery concrete race-track, producing the most spectacular efforts at four-legged braking as they approached the barriers at either end. They cannoned into them and into each other with gay abandon before fighting all the way back to the other end, and repeating the performance.

If for any reason the gates were open at either end the liberated animals would disappear at full pace across our landlord's winter barley crop, looking from afar rather like a pack of clumsy hounds in full pursuit of a fox. Or they would threaten to use the larger slurry pit as a swimming pool, the braver natural leaders among them performing a wonderful

belly-flop into the steamy liquid. They then had to be horribly rescued from the revolting depths. By the time they were all rounded up and sorted out – and try sorting out sixty-odd pigs now all covered in the same lookalike slime, slashed with reddening teeth marks and bruises – I at least had long ceased to see the funny side of anything.

Every two or three days Paul used to scrape this outside area with a tractor and rear-mounted scraper, pushing the mess of dung, urine and rainwater along the length, then up a slight ramp, and slosh into the slurry pit, taking care not to follow it with the tractor, which could have been very nasty. One day Paul, mistakenly assuming Alan's competence as a tractor driver from the way he used the A10 as though it were an extension of Brands Hatch, gave this job to Alan. He had to manoeuvre the tractor with its eight-foot-wide scraper backwards from one end into the nine-foot-wide dung channel, which was bounded by the building on one side, and a three-foot-high wall on the other. The ground behind this small wall sloped up to the field.

Alan leapt with confidence onto the tractor, and Paul went on with the chores inside. He could hear the tractor engine from there, but after a while realised all had gone very quiet. Just as he was getting worried, there came the noise of a fiercely revving engine, then once again uneasy quiet. In a few moments a sheepish Alan appeared in the building, having somehow managed to miss the entrance to the channel altogether, shoot up the wrong side of the retaining wall, and finish up with the tractor and scraper wedged against this wall, which had fortunately prevented it from falling over. Paul had the devil's

39

own job to extricate the tractor from this difficult situation, for the scraper was wider than the tractor and was jammed into the earth on one side, and the bottom of the wall on the other. Both he and Alan regarded it as quite a jolly adventure.

But this minor mishap paled into insignificance when compared with the trail of destruction wrought by a headmaster friend of mine who had kindly offered to help with my harvest. On one glorious occasion, when armed with a tractor and trailer, he succeeded in demolishing an eighteen-inch brick pillar and a four-foot section of nine-inch wall. He then ran over and flattened a wheelbarrow and finally, when crossing a rough field too fast (to make up for lost time), vibrated the trailer pin out. Trailer and tractor parted company, pulling the connected hydraulic pipe messily from its socket as they did so, and leaving the trailer drawbar embedded in the furrow it had created by its uncontrolled forward movement. Oil was everywhere.

As my friend was at that time, for a favour, providing me with teaching experience in a futile effort to broaden my outlook, I could really only smile weakly and make some inane remark like: 'Don't worry. It happens to all of us.' Which may be true, but is of small consolation at the time.

Apart from Alan, we had another regular helper from Paul's past, a research chemist. Brian came to help Paul every Saturday morning and would plod quietly on in his outsize wellies, specialising in cleaning out the smaller pens, for a very modest sum which he squandered on beer after hockey in the afternoon. He assured us he was happy to work on the farm for such token remuneration to 'give him a change'. As he spent the rest of the week in an office or laboratory beavering away at whatever it is research chemists beaver away at, and as he did not have the most robust physique, he fairly quickly, as he himself admitted, became 'knackered'. What he must have been like by the time he left the field of play later in the afternoon I dread to think.

As a casual worker our one failure was the son of a friend of mine, who implored me to give him a holiday job to save him getting completely square eyes. I passed him on to Paul, who, to break him in gently, gave him the relatively easy job of helping to unload bales, considerably putting him on the trailer where he could roll them off. He was a strapping youth, dressed in impeccable jeans and T-shirt, who told us impressive stories of his athletic prowess, though as the day wore on he became progressively quieter and more reflective, and certainly dirtier and sweatier. We gave him food, and let him off early. Later that evening I received a rather pathetic phone call from him, saying he did not think he could come again and that 'the work wasn't quite as I imagined' and 'I do not really feel I can cope any more.' This sad incident – I am not used to rejection after a few hours – emphasised to me how much harder than most the farm worker cheerfully works, without complaint or fuss; as well as how coddled and cushioned much of our youth is today.

Our other casual workers, good as they were, could only help when their other more remunerative occupations allowed. What we needed was more permanent help. Just at that time, one of my own part-time lads, who was going on to university the following autumn (yes, I know, we do seem to specialise in educated types), asked for a job for the rest of the year.

Nick was willing and keen, and had been quite satisfactory with me, apart from holding the most outrageous left-wing views. He adamantly refused to agree with my sensible and reasoned arguments for the introduction of the death penalty for strikers, flogging for shoplifters, transportation for the unemployed, and other worthy causes. He was inclined to be a trifle wayward in his approach, especially to machinery, which he regarded with a certain amount of academic disdain, but at least he was used to pigs and their ways. So we suggested that he join Paul for a spell, to which he readily agreed.

Once Paul had introduced Nick to the intricacies of the pipeline system, explained and demonstrated the routine to him, stocked up with whey, concentrate and barley, and reduced the numbers to manageable proportions, he felt it safe to treat himself to a long-awaited break, it being over a year since he had had a full day off.

Paul planned a weekend canal trip with a group of friends, and one Friday evening, leaving all placid and serene, set off for the rendezvous, which he reached two hours later. Having downed his first freedom pint in the pub, he rang up to check that all was well, to be greeted by the news that all was chaos. Apparently the pipeline system, obviously cross that Paul had

abandoned it, had refused to work. Nick had panicked, fetched out Paul's wife (who had sensibly stayed at home, not relishing weekend cooking for hungry inebriates drifting up, or down, or in, a canal), also Paul's neighbour, and anyone else he could think of who might know something about obstreperous hurdy-gurdies. Fortunately, I was away.

As is so often the case, Paul knew instantly what the trouble was from the described symptoms, a minor air-lock in a valve, and could explain to Nick what to do. But fearing something else might go wrong, Paul, having poured himself aboard that night, the next morning left his mates sleeping it off and walked with throbbing head from their mooring to the nearest phone box, which turned out to be all of three miles away, to check that all was well. Which praise be, it was.

After this inauspicious start, Nick settled down pretty well, and at the least gave Paul someone to talk to, other than the stock.

Nick's main drawback was that he managed never to have more than a few pence on him when he went to the pub with Paul, and he always said he had to save that in case he ran out of petrol on the way home; so Paul found himself not only paying his wages, which he could ill afford, but for his beer also. Nick also had the occasional lapse of concentration, which was not usually that serious, but led him once to drive the tractor straight off the gravel drive for no obvious reason, being rescued from the hedge in a state of puzzled bewilderment.

That aberration apart, Nick proved a jovial help-mate until he ascended to pastures academic and the physical (at least) cleanliness of student politics.

Apart from giving Paul the opportunity for the occasional day off, even though his exit from the slurry-smeared driveway was usually the signal for all hell to break loose, one of our main reasons for employing Nick was to give us a hand with our expansion programme.

For, in spite of all our dramas and traumas, our first year at The Piggery had really been quite successful. I hasten to add that this was not because of any particular expertise on our part, but because we had been lucky enough to enjoy reasonable pig prices and low food costs, the two essential ingredients of profitability. Our original optimistic aim had been to try and establish our joint enterprise financially by putting a large number of fattening pigs through the unit. We would then pursue our longer-term aim, which was to establish a self-contained breeding and fattening unit, Paul being keen to try his charms on young ladies of the four-legged kind, as well as the other kind.

We had been, as we later appreciated, very lucky to have had a mild first winter. Under propitious conditions the rent we were paying was a moderate one, we had decent suppliers of stock, and supportive buyers of our porkers and cutters. After the usual juggling with figures to achieve the mutually incompatible aims of keeping the bank manager happy without paying too much tax, we showed a profit of some eight thousand pounds (before remuneration), which we, though I doubt if many would, regarded as a satisfactory reward for our efforts. If only we had possessed a crystal ball, we should have got out while the going was good. Instead, we pressed on.

Among the many buildings in a state of semi-decay which flanked The Piggery rather like grimy and rusty tugs around a battleship, was a square breeze-block and asbestos structure. Internally, half of this had been converted to farrowing pens, and it was here that Paul ambitiously decided to start his breeding herd, relying on information gleaned from specialist literature and good advice from neighbours to put him right.

By counting such important attributes as heads (one), legs (four), teats (twelve), and testicles (two), we selected from among our existing stock – for we could not afford to buy in – a number of gilts and a boar, the latter hopefully one of those with heterosexual rather than homosexual tendencies. (We seemed to harbour a predominantly gay community.) Fortunately Bruno turned out to be the male equivalent of a nymphomaniac, and was often to be seen collapsed in a corner of his pen, exhausted by his over-enthusiastic labours.

Paul and Nick made some rudimentary improvements to the farrowing quarters, putting in such necessities as creeps and rails. We also tried to warm the place up a bit by plugging some of the gaps in the walls, which appeared to have been constructed by an amateur bricklayer with a thick head on an off-day. Moreover, the wooden door to the building sagged on its hinges, scraped the ground and was difficult to latch. Many were the times that Paul came round the corner to find this door gaping open, and several of the more adventurous gilts foraging around outside with that particular piggy earnestness, allied to a stubborn refusal to return whence they came until coaxed in by the bribe of extra food.

After a number of false starts by our enthusiastic but inexperienced boar who, though he recognised the opposite sex, got rather confused about ends, ways, and means – indeed, he appeared to have no particular preference – Paul managed to get our maiden gilts in pig. Well, most of them. Two later proved to have been but a snare and a delusion. In the fullness of time our first litter arrived. Towards the end of this pregnancy Paul gave every indication of distraught fatherhood,

44

going about his duties with an abstracted air, and nipping round the corner to check on his labouring 'wife' every few minutes. Of course, in the end she farrowed when he was not there, producing quite a nice litter of nine, and earning Bruno the first of his many awards for endeavour.

This initial effort at breeding was designed as a trial run to give Paul some necessary experience. In a way it was a false dawn, for it looked too easy. That first gilt, for instance, reared eight out of those nine piglets. We lived to regret that Paul could not have learned on someone else's farm and at someone else's expense, for sheer ignorance and ineptitude cost us dear over the years. Successful breeding is a highly complex operation, requiring meticulous attention to detail, and a high level of all-round knowledge and stockmanship. Good intentions are not enough, and a most competent and attractive adviser from the MLC (Meat and Livestock Commission) forcefully attempted over the years to correct our most glaring mistakes. We were, I believe, modest enough to accept her strictures with due humility. It would have been most amusing for an outsider to see Paul and me sitting in the corner being lectured to by this stern and youthful mentor, rather like naughty schoolboys who have made a hash of their exam papers.

If we had any desire to defend ourselves to her from the charge of gross dereliction of duty – which we had not, though not unnaturally money, or lack of it, had always been one of the reasons for our poor performance – the harsh statement that although we were not actually her worst producers, we were not far from it, would be enough to crush us into the ground again. The one thing we did appear to have got right was the quality of the porkers we sold, which graded well and commanded a premium payment.

Among those first few gilts there were, as always, a number of great characters. The animal who, without any bother at all, produces a litter of seventeen and then promptly eats them all, and the one who perversely produces only three, and then fails to supply even them with enough mother's milk are common in many herds. We do not usually speak about them, and get rid of them just as quickly as we decently can. But we had one or two exceptional loonies.

There was, for instance, the Hurdler. From a standing start

she could clear the four-foot wall of her pen without any trouble. If she had room for a run, her capacity was almost unlimited. Every morning Paul would find her out of her pen and happily browsing among the chewed meal bags and scattered tools. She would trot quite readily back into her pen, swaying sideways to avoid Paul's boot, and with a look which plainly said: 'You'll never keep *me* in you know.' She did, however, overreach herself one day when, in a moment of optimism, she tried to clear not only the pen wall, but the creep area beneath it, an obstacle rather like the Chair at Aintree. Great screams of frustration brought Paul running, to find her balanced precariously on wall and creep rail, teetering back and forward like a seesaw. A lusty heave to her rear quarters helped her into the next pen, but this was the last straw, and the next day she departed to the sausage factory, where I am sure she tried to jump out of the skins!

Then there was the Masochistic Boar. He was being schooled as an understudy to our lecherous first string. Needless to say, Bruno did not take at all kindly to this reflection on his sexual powers, being fully confident – with some justification – that he could personally manage any number of partners. At the earliest opportunity he attempted to settle the hash of this upstart newcomer. A dreadful battle ensued, the new recruit refusing to give best, in spite of considerable disadvantage in height, weight and reach. By the time Paul managed to part the combatants they were both exhausted and ready for a truce – as was Paul, who found out what it must be like to be the referee of a wrestling match trying to part two fighters who are both determined to ignore you and carry on scrapping.

Perhaps because of this unnerving encounter, Joe decided that he much preferred the company of the opposite sex and, in competition with the Hurdler, time and again scaled the walls between two intervening pens to join a bunch of attractive gilts. Unfortunately, they violently objected to this male presence, and poor ol' Joe was as often beaten up, and left wounded and bleeding in a corner; presumably being too gallant, or too overwhelmed, to fight back.

Rescued by Paul he would be returned to his individual casualty clearing station, only to be found next morning yet again among his unwelcoming harem, who had all been well

THE OLD PIGGERY

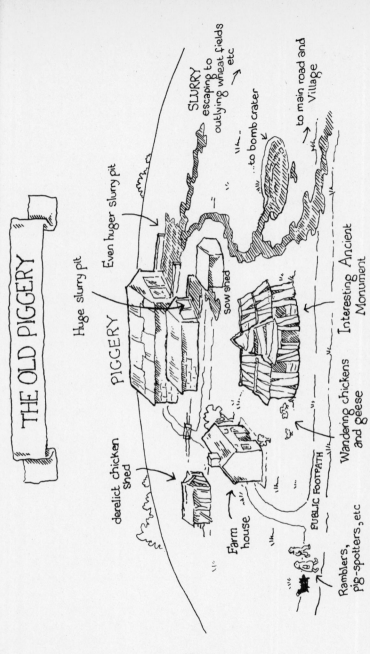

Huge slurry pit

Even huger slurry pit

SLURRY
escaping to
outlying wheat fields
etc

...to bomb crater

to main road and
Village

PIGGERY

Sow shed

derelict chicken
shed

Interesting Ancient
Monument

Farm
house

PUBLIC FOOTPATH

Wandering chickens
and geese

Ramblers,
pig-spotters, etc

47

served – in more ways than one – two or three to be exact – by Bruno, obviously their ideal as a mate.

Joe would lie quite happily with any female, however misogamistical she might be, and indeed proved an able deputy to Bruno, though lacking his senior's panache. But as soon as he was on his own he was impossible to contain. At least, he was in our building, in which any unusual activity rocked the foundations, and where the walls and doors were beginning to show all too obvious signs of abuse. Never a very prepossessing structure, after a few months' misuse by a group of randy males, itinerant females and their progeny – who learned how to squeeze under their doors in a matter of hours from birth – it looked as though it had been given the once over by a gang of vandals. We carefully hid our aerosol sprays to stop such graffiti as 'Humans are *NOT* pigs'.

As we really only occupied this building on sufferance, and there were increasing tensions over our tenancy agreement, Joe had to go to meet his maker. It was with some regret that we watched him limp up the ramp of the lorry, bruised but unbowed by his most recent going-over, and ready, I am sure, to snuggle in with any piggy angel (female) who would have him. I hope he found 'the Hurdler'.

Chapter Six

'This little piggy went to market. This little piggy stayed at home.' (Anon.)

COME THE AUTUMN, Nick mounted his motor scooter for the last time and with a cheerful wave pop-popped off to further education, leaving Paul to cope with The Piggery on his own once more. And what a traumatic time he was to have of it! Our efforts to improve ventilation and so on for the better creature comforts of our piggy non-paying guests during a hot spell had proved pretty ineffective. Our preparations for what was to be an extremely cold winter were even more futile. The great, gaunt bulk of The Piggery, perched on the top of a bare hill and exposed to winds from heaven and, naked to the elements, remained completely indifferent to our puny attempts to create cosy sleeping areas and to protect both man and beast, not to mention machine, from the fury of the elements.

On New Year's Day of our second winter we woke to deep snow and freezing temperatures. Paul leapt from his warm couch to find frost on the inside of the windows of his unheated cottage, and jumped into his van to drive to The Piggery. After fifty yards or so he stuck fast in a snowdrift in the high-banked lane. Floundering back to the cottage he borrowed his wife's Mini to try another route.

'Where are you going with my car?' asked a plaintive voice from the bedroom window as the starter whirred painfully in slow motion.

'You go back to bed and stay there,' replied Paul. 'Ring up and tell your clients they'll have to cope with life without you for a day or two.' This time he got as far as the entrance to the farm drive before finishing up in another snow drift.

There were two vehicles abandoned, and half a mile to go to The Piggery, where eight hundred animals, fed up with waiting for their grub, were letting the surrounding neighbourhood

49

know in no uncertain terms that they were getting impatient. Their screams and yells shattered the frozen air and bounced over the snowy landscape as Paul plodded through the snow towards them, reflecting that at least they were keeping their vocal cords warm.

His arrival was greeted by a sustained outburst of noise which threatened to lift the roof and shatter his eardrums. Rather like, Paul reflected, the sort of reception which greeted The Beatles as they pranced on stage. The scene which met him was catastrophic. Whipped by high winds the snow had blown through the roof vents, between the Yorkshire boarding, and under the asbestos sheets. A light film covered not only pens but pigs as well. Perhaps because they were the coldest part of the body, snow had settled and frozen on the snouts of the animals, and these white tips above slobbering jaws made them look like some strange new breed. The 'Pauline New Spot', I suggested later.

Much worse was to follow. Hoping to quell the threatened mutiny by satisfying the pigs' hunger, Paul ran to start the mixer. The pump was frozen and the motor could not start it. The water in the tank supplying the mixer was frozen. All the several dozen valves in the pipeline were frozen. On this first day of the cold spell it took Paul several hours with blowtorch, hammer, bad language and perseverance to get the whole hurdy-gurdy working.

By that time even the pigs had given up hope, and had retired to the corners of their sleeping pens, where they lay huddled in untidy heaps surrounded by moisture from their thawing backs and their steamy breath. Occasionally a malevolent eye would open in the midst of the pile and would regard Paul's progress with disdain, as he struggled to free the frozen pipe above them. But all ennui disappeared the moment Paul at long last got the mixer to work. With shrieks of anticipation the heaps erupted into their constituent parts; with the exception of the smaller, weaker members of the community, who by now had had more than enough of being sat on, dripped on and trodden on, and who, poor things, lay where they were in pathetic postures. By the time they had stirred their stumps to stagger to the trough, there was, of course, nothing but the smell left, and they could only nose disconsolately around in the nooks and crannies for any tiny morsel.

50

This first day was easy compared with what was to follow. Paul could only get backwards and forwards by using the tractor, as it was several days before the roads were opened, and then the farm drive was still impassable. No feed lorry could get through, and bags of concentrate had to be ferried the half-mile to the buildings. (Paul remembers actually carrying bags on his back that distance, but cannot remember exactly why.)

Any visitor was immediately coerced into helping with the daily – sometimes twice-daily – thawing-out process. One of these arrived home on leave from Kuwait, and nearly perished in the cold which he considered a much worse hardship than the Arab ban on booze. Another friend, on leave from his post with an oil company, was rather too enthusiastically entertained in Alan's pub by Alan and Paul. The revellers spent the night on the floor of the bar, then early next morning Alan and Paul persuaded their friend to accompany them to The Piggery to help thaw out. On the way they stopped for a too-greasy breakfast in a roadside cafe. On arrival at The Piggery, frozen in snowy solitude, the friend found out too late that he was allergic to the smell of pigs. He unceremoniously returned his breakfast, and spent the rest of the morning white-faced in the car well down the lane with the engine running and the heater on; the while Alan and Paul dashed backwards and forwards

51

with blowtorch and gas bottle, and our eight hundred pigs screamed their impatience. For, not only did all the connections freeze up nightly, but the pipeline itself froze if the tiniest drop of wet meal was left in it. One of the most difficult problems was in a section of pipe which we had carefully insulated by surrounding it with straw bales. The bales did not prevent freezing, and most of the stack had to be demolished to get at the pipe.

After several days of increasingly severe frost and fresh snowfalls, when even brass monkeys were taking evasive action, Paul had to abandon the pipeline feeding altogether. All the pigs had to be fed dry meal from a bag, and water had to be carried in buckets from the farmhouse, our own supply having frozen solid. It was virtually impossible to satisfy their needs, let alone carry out any of the normal duties, like mucking out. In any case, the dunging passage was a sheet of thin brown ice, and if any of the pigs did get out there they found themselves performing involuntary splits in the best four-legged naked ballet tradition.

One or two seemed to enjoy it after the initial surprise, and perfected variations, which mainly consisted of slithering along the ice on their bottoms with a look of intense pleasure on their faces. The boars particularly took to this pastime.

One helpful spin-off was that the slurry pit froze over. Strangely enough, given our record for such events, nobody actually fell through the ice. When time permitted we were able to lower the level by removing great blocks of ice with the rear-loader. It was, of course, just a temporary reprieve, for

every slight thaw brought a fresh influx of by now very con-
centrated slurry, and the pits overflowed with all their old
enthusiasm, sending an embarrassing flow of liquid sludge all
too obviously through deep brown channels in the pristine snow
to the road.

Unlike nearly all disasters, the big freeze-up does not diminish
in agony the further away it gets. Our set-backs and losses
were horrendous, particularly from pigs damaging legs and
joints in the cold, and infection affecting their bones, in spite of
numerous jabs of that miracle drug, penicillin, and their
removal to our hospital ward. Once the joints became well
swollen we found it almost impossible to get the sufferers back
on their feet, and the local knacker man enjoyed a temporary
boom in supply, which presumably did him some good, but us
none at all.

You can well imagine, after such a summer and winter, allied
to a continuing fall in pig prices and an EEC-induced rise in
grain prices, that when we were confronted by our landlord
with a request for a one hundred per cent rent increase, we
were not at all receptive. This really put us on the spot, for we
were struggling to survive in what has always been a 'free'
market for pigmeat, subject to periodical booms and slumps.
The latter were often induced by subsidised imports from the
continent, and aggravated by the artificially high support price
for cereals, which has since resulted in the notorious grain
mountain.

The proposed rent increase was not really as unreasonable a
demand as it might appear. We had to admit that we had
'enjoyed' the use of a vast amount of space for a pretty moderate
rent for some time. Presumably, our landlords felt that we had
had a fair crack of the whip, and that it was high time they had
a bit of jam, besides a lot of smell, disturbance and the
involuntary involvement in some of our more public dramas.

A mass break-out by a group of young offenders across fifty
acres of newly sown wheat springs graphically to mind. This
was immediately after a heavy thunderstorm (do pigs get
frightened by thunder and crawl under the settee as dogs do?)
which had the twin effects of quickly reducing their woofing
gallop to a laborious trot while at the same time creating the
most almighty mess on the field. Paul hid in shame when our

landlord next appeared at the farm and prayed that he would not choose that moment to inspect the adjacent field. Sadly, he did, and it was quite obvious from the way he walked to his Land-Rover and slammed the door that he was not at all thrilled by the look of his crop.

'I'm ever so sorry,' apologised Paul. 'I'll roll it for you when it gets dry.' A grunt and a shower of gravel was the only reply.

The rent increase was formally proposed at a meeting between our landlord and his wife and Paul and me in the former's luxury farmhouse. This was quite a friendly meeting, during which Paul and I consumed as much of our host's whisky as we could get hold of, feeling it might be our last chance, but even through the self-induced alcoholic haze it was clear that our increasingly strident pleading of hard times and harder to come – how right we were! – were falling on deaf ears. In the end it was left that we would think it over, and we departed in a mood of some depression.

For it had become obvious that our second year was going to be about half as prosperous as our first; which meant that, as usual with ailing businesses, those two vital balance sheet items which our nationalised industries always seem fit to ignore, rent and bank charges, would figure more prominently than the earnings of the humble working participants. As we all should know, a high gearing ratio (or whatever the technical term is) of the servicing charges of borrowed money to potential income is a danger signal. The red lights were certainly beginning to flash in our direction.

With the approach of the deadline of the renewal of our tenancy agreement, Paul and I tried to draw up a balance sheet of the pros and cons of staying at The Piggery. In spite of the fact that if Paul had stayed in industry he would by now have been earning a substantial salary instead of a miserable pittance, and that neither of us had yet received any return for the capital we had invested, the thought of giving up never occurred to us. It was simply a matter of where and how we carried on.

Many of the drawbacks of The Piggery I have already described. These were compounded by our own inexperience and, let's face it, our inefficiency, and also by the stubborn refusal of our landlords to spend a penny on the place, plus an apparent indifference to what was going on, unless they were directly affected. The buildings were, after all, remote from their main farm, and problems of slurry disposal, unless you actually tramp through the overflow every day, or live within sight and smell of the stuff, do not appear that urgent from a safe distance.

Against that we had to weigh the fact that The Piggery was isolated (a big advantage) and big enough to provide enormous potential as a unit. But for us to realise that potential required a deal of further investment. The Piggery was a rented unit with no security of tenure (because we had agreed to give up if requested, and we did not intend to renege on this agreement), and we were unenthusiastic about investing any more borrowed money unless our landlord also spent money on the unit, which he obviously had no intention of doing.

A main disadvantage from our point of view was that Paul did not live on the place. The perpetual journeyings to and fro were an expensive time-waster, but it also meant that we could never really know what was going on all the time. Paul lived in dread of what he would find – or not find – when he got there. On one heart-stopping occasion he was some half-way to the unit when he was confronted by a group of sows on the road, some of whom were in an advanced state of pregnancy, and none of whom had read the Highway Code. Paul leapt from his van and frantically started herding these errant females into a nearby field before he realised that they were not, in fact, his. So he contented himself with shutting the gate on them, to the obvious alarm of the incumbents, a pair of aged riding horses, and with some quiet satisfaction alerting the rightful owner when he reached a telephone at The Piggery.

The pleasant couple who did live on the place were normally helpful and friendly; suppliers of hot water for defreezing and coffee for visitors. But they were inclined to treat the place and our eight hundred or so pigs as though they were theirs, and to show all and sundry around the unit with proprietorial pride, until we put a firm stop to it. Also, in spite of constant pleading, they would allow their various farm animals, principally chickens with incipient diarrhoea, to roam all over the place. Not unnaturally, the favourite scratching and feeding area was in our meal store (which was part of a large open Dutch barn)

55

and around the mixer, the hopper of which the chickens seemed to regard as their private lavatory.

Paul would arrive to find, to his intense annoyance, a gang of these feathered pests creating mayhem among his expensive concentrates and playing their own version of catch-me-if-you-can around the whey tank, over the wet-pit, and among the empty meal bags. He would rush at them with a great shout, hurling anything at them which came to hand. The chickens would respond with infuriated squawking, noisily flying away from him to the security of the pen walls and the walkways of The Piggery.

This would upset the pigs, who would rush around their pens barking excitedly, bashing into each other, doing the splits, and generally trying to damage themselves. This behaviour would quickly spread right through the long building, each pen in turn taking up the cause, until the whole vast area was pulsating with frenzy. It was an excellent example of what the textbooks call a 'stress factor'. I do not know what it did to the pigs, but it certainly did not do my blood pressure any good.

Such incidents inevitably led to a certain amount of tension and ill-feeling, and just occasionally this would boil over into direct action. As, for instance, the day Paul arrived to find that for some misdemeanour – real or imagined – one of his voluntary assistants had been pelted with eggs, and had regrettably responded by throwing pig muck over the car of his attacker. As you will imagine, it took quite a lot of tact and free pork before normal relations were resumed.

Unfortunately, too, a footpath passed right through the farm.

This would not have been too bad if all the walkers had stuck to the path, but a number of the more curious of the brethren of country-lovers seemed to regard the walkways of The Piggery as extensions of their rural promenade. This was a constant worry for us, as not all users of rights-of-way are kindly disposed towards farmers, especially if they possess that bête noire of the liberal and progressive thinker, an intensive unit. Moreover, every intrusion from farm or footpath into our unit made a mockery of any of our precautions designed to prevent the spread of disease.

Among the many 'cons' were the facts that the unit was bleak and cold, and also pipeline and slurry based. Not surprisingly, as time passed Paul had become increasingly disillusioned with this set-up, and more and more enamoured of my own simple system of straw yards and ad-lib feeders; which although not necessarily as efficient as more elaborate (and expensive) set-ups, was at least labour-saving.

Restricted pipeline feeding, which had been recommended *ad nauseum* to us by trim-suited experts, has the great disadvantage that it has to be operated twice a day, every day. On a one-man, non-automatic unit this can be pretty onerous, especially if that one man plays rugger and enjoys a few beers afterwards. In a confessional moment Paul admitted to me that on occasions after some famous victory, come eight o'clock in the evening he had been puzzled to remember whether he had been back to feed the pigs, or whether he still had to do it. A detour of some ten miles to The Piggery while en route to the Chinese take-away was not at all popular with his club-mates, though being rugger players they took it all in good heart.

In a sense we felt that we were surviving where we were on borrowed time, not to mention borrowed money. The pig market was collapsing; food costs were rising inexorably, while world prices slumped. Moreover, the pigs had a dysentery problem which no amount of expensive medication seemed to improve. Once established, swine dysentery is the very devil to eradicate, particularly in a unit such as ours with a constant throughput and the virtual impossibility of isolating individual pens – basically because of our continuous dung passage. If not actually fatal – which it often is – swine dysentery makes a nonsense of any projected growth rates. In addition, one of our

57

weaner suppliers had gone out of business, and we were having a job keeping the unit full, being reluctant to buy from other sources.

Eventually, we reached the same conclusion independently. One day I drove to The Piggery to find Paul, assisted by Nick, who was earning a few bob on vacation, struggling to unblock the discharge pipe from the slurry tanker. This had the unfortunate habit of either stuffing itself full of detritus from the floor of the slurry pit, and then refusing to ejaculate, or becoming detached from the parent body altogether and losing interest in the whole operation.

Nick was knee-deep in the slurry pit poking up the pipe in a forlorn way with the broken shaft of a pitchfork. Paul was on the tractor attempting to make the obstinate machine suck. Unfortunately, he had forgotten that the mechanism was set to spread, not suck. As he raced the tractor engine and released the clutch for the umpteenth time, the tanker decided enough was enough, gave an almighty fart, and sprayed Nick from head to foot with a foul-smelling liquid hot from the bogs of The Piggery.

Poor Nick! It took him several days to get rid of the stink from his thick curly hair. He was only allowed into the 'above stairs' of the family home upon condition that he did not stay long, and even more seriously, he did not dare go into his favourite local. His immediate humiliation was not helped by the

hysterical laughter of his two employers, or by Paul philo-sophically remarking, 'At least the machine is working again.'

It had, apparently, been one of those days. As soon as Paul had got to the unit in the morning and started the feeding routine he had been disconcerted to find one pen completely empty, all the pigs having made a united bid for freedom by forcing the door open to the dunging passage, and then *shutting it behind them*. Fortunately the gates at either end of the dunging passage were shut and they were confined in that area, where they could now be heard yelling and screaming because they could not get back to their breakfast.

To add insult to injury Paul also discovered a casualty in another pen, the victim (apparently) of whey bloat; while the evening before a couple of those itinerant diddicoy/scrap-metal dealers had been foolishly directed round to The Piggery to find Paul, who was, of course, out. Not surprisingly, two of his precious weaners had gone missing, presumably to feature as suckling pig on the Sunday menu in a caravan in a distant lay-by. We imagined the enticing smell of roast pork wafting among the car bodies which were being dissected to their saleable parts by, we also feared, some of our tools. It is an inescapable fact that few farmers seem to know exactly how many tools they possess at any given moment, or where they might be. Paul, as casual as most, was adept at doing an emergency repair, laying the tools down to resume whatever operation had been interrupted, and then forgetting all about them until too late. In the interim the tools were consumed, knocked down in the dung, or just spirited away.

I listened to this tale of woe as we sat on straw bales, drinking tepid coffee from Paul's flask and keeping well to windward of Nick. We mutually agreed that the time had come to move to pastures new.

This was the watershed in our joint enterprise. After much discussion over the next few days, we concluded that if we had to pay some £4500 per year in rent, which was the sum demanded, we might just as well pay that amount in bank charges and try to buy a more suitable unit. This would at least have the merit of being our own one day. (We thought.) Perhaps that was not very sophisticated economic reasoning, but it seemed sensible at the time.

We began to study properties for sale in the farming press. We went to look at a number of what – in print – appeared possibilities. We were quickly disillusioned. Our basic requirements were a house of some sort, buildings with at least the potential of housing enough pigs to keep one man busy, and a small area of land to allow for expansion, dung disposal, and so on. We were anxious to keep out of the notorious, over-populated and disease-prone East Anglian triangle, where I was already involved in a unit. With my conviction that pigs should not have a long journey to slaughter, a handy and reliable abattoir was desirable – not at all easy to find, with abattoirs disappearing even faster than pig farmers. The new unit should be within commuting distance of my own Hertford-shire farm, preferably near a racecourse so that my visits could combine business with pleasure and, hopefully, at least the travelling expenses of my racing activities be tax-deductible.

Within these quite modest limitations we soon found out that our budgeted forty thousand pounds was just not enough, though it might well be today, following the dramatic fall in land values. For this sort of sum we were offered a number of units in advanced stages of decay, the wind whistling forlornly through bungalows built of what appeared to be materials from a scrapyard, stirring up leaves and dust and flapping the sackcloth in buildings where all maintenance had long since been abandoned, together presumably with the hopes of the previous owners. These places were profoundly depressing, and we had to face up to the fact that we would not be able to service the borrowings necessary to set them to rights; and we still had to obtain the blessing of our friendly bank manager.

Moreover, none of the units we looked over left us feeling at all enthusiastic. They were usually in unsatisfactory places; too close to potential hazards like fussy neighbours, or stuck in the middle of a desolate prairie, ventilated by icy blasts direct from the Antarctic, or up a long muddy track guarded by the barking Alsatians of cottagers who seemed to deal in tenth-hand cars. If the buildings were in any way acceptable they were usually slurry based, and we both felt we had seen quite enough slurry to last us a lifetime. If the house was habitable, it was either too big or too small, or the owners had regarded cats as more important than mere humans, or it was downwind from the pig unit. If the whole unit had potential it was way beyond our figure.

As we were nursing the frustrations common to all property seekers, certain developments occurred. It might be going too far to believe as Henry Miller does 'that through being receptive, keeping one's mind and heart open – showing faith and trust in other words – one's desires, or prayers, are realised,' to explain 'the part of fortune'. But something like that did happen at this important moment of our lives. Firstly, the tenants of a bungalow on my farm reluctantly gave notice, their work taking them to another area. At the same time the manager of the firm who hired my chicken unit (for rearing pullets) informed me that he was looking for a more satisfactory worker than the rather gormless youth they had been employing, who, like so many products of our educational system, needed constant supervision. Even then, he frequently forgot what he was meant to be doing, and when he did remember, he did it wrong.

With one of those flashes of inspiration which I occasionally have – usually in the middle of the night – I glimpsed a possible solution to our future. 'Eureka,' I whispered (it being 3.00 am). The next morning I suggested to Paul that we should build a new unit on the ground adjacent to the chicken unit, so that existing roads and services could be used; that he should move into the bungalow; and that he should offer himself to the poultry firm as a part-time employee.

This arrangement had many advantages. We would save the cost of the land. Paul would have suitable accommodation and some income to tide him over the transition period. The buildings would be to our own design – we had ideas and illusions of our competence in that direction – and as they would be on an existing farm they would qualify for grant aid (then 22½ per cent of approved costs). The big snag from Paul's point of view was that he would be very much in my pocket, and, at least to start with, would not have much of an ownership stake in the unit or in the house, as it would belong to me, and our joint company would only occupy it and trade from it.

However, if we were ever to give up The Piggery for something more practicable and convenient it was really Hobson's choice. We approached our landlord, who displayed no

61

perceptible emotion, but sportingly agreed to let us continue a month or so after our tenancy agreement expired. We hoped this would enable us to start in the new buildings with dysentery-free stock.

With much trepidation we went to see our bank manager in his wall-to-safe carpeted inner sanctum. He looked down from his white horse – he was inclined to take his duties a little too seriously – listened politely to the optimistic noises we made while polishing his boots, and encouraged us to go ahead. (Actually, he was on to a good thing. For this was in effect just further development on a farm which he already held as security.) The chicken company made no objection to our scheme, having checked there were no diseases transmissible between pigs and chickens, and agreed to take on Paul when he moved. We were well and truly embarked upon the second phase of our partnership.

THE NEW PIGGERY

Here continueth . . .

Having, dear brethren, not only erred in many ways, but also left undone many things that we should have done (like the gates to the slurry channel), we finally strayed towards The New Piggery. Where dwelt hope eternal. But not, as yet, in a terrestrial building.

Our journey there resembled in travail that of the pilgrim, Christian. He, however, made it.

Chapter Seven

'I never know what I do, but I seem to spend all day doing it.' (L. Parry)

THERE IS an old English saying that he who relies upon the completion date promised by a builder deserves to be kept waiting. The Ancient Briton who chiselled these words of wisdom in the rock wall of his mother-in-law's overcrowded cave was probably frustrated at the delays in the erection of his detached mud and wattle in a downtown clearing, having been told for the umpteenth time that cow-pats were in short supply. The cow-pat makers had gone on strike, demanding less time and motion and more buffalo meat and mead.

When Paul was at long last able to put stock into the new building on our new site, he knew how that Brit felt. As usual, we managed to get it all wrong. For a start, in September, when we made the momentous decision to give up The Piggery, we fondly imagined that the new unit (hereinafter referred to as 'The New Piggery') would be in operation by the turn of the year. Whereas, if we had been sensible, and in spite of Parkinson's Law that 'work expands so as to fill the time available for its completion,' we should have allowed at least another three months. We should also have guessed that we would get the wettest autumn and the coldest December for years.

However, full of enthusiasm and get-up-and-go we optimistically cut the first sod. Or rather, we persuaded a neighbour, aided and abetted by a wayward Drott bulldozer, to clear the proposed site of the remnants of a Christmas tree enterprise. This had originally been planned to expand by an acre a year. The labour of weeding, the depredations of rabbits and muntjak deer, the long growing time, and the derisory price offered for the end product, had soon persuaded us to abandon the scheme. For some time we had been selling the trees off piecemeal to whoever would come and remove them.

As soon as Paul and I had received the blessing of our helpful bank manager we started to make enquiries for the type of building we had in mind as the nucleus of our new unit. We accepted a quote for a steel-framed building, which was, to my regret, much cheaper than a concrete equivalent, which I would have preferred. In my own concrete and asbestos pig barns such steel parts as there were had rusted away to the thinness of cardboard. This was due partly I suppose to the permanently tainted breath of the inhabitants, who only ever appear to clean their teeth upon each other; not to mention their complete disregard of any of the niceties of toilet discipline so essential in a well-run piggery.

To extract the roots of thousands of truncated Christmas trees our contractor adapted a sub-soiler behind his Drott. This proved most effective, but unfortunately also brought to the surface broken portions of a land drain, which I had forgotten lay under this piece of land. By the time we had repaired this and disposed of the roots and stumps in large fires, which seemed to smoulder for ever – and incidentally brought us a rebuke from the Gas Board, who had spied from their weekly helicopter inspection that we were burning over the route of one of their pipelines – the building was well overdue. Many phone calls and three weeks later it arrived upon a lorry so large that even after an orgy of shunting, shouting, and swearing it was unable to get onto the site.

In the end Paul gave up and just told the driver to drive his juggernaut over the corner of the hedge, and we would later widen the concrete apron of the existing entrance to correspond. In a perverse sort of way there is nothing more satisfying than seeing huge wheels crunching through undergrowth to clear a path for modern progress. It was not quite so satisfying when those same huge wheels slowly and deliberately squashed flat a number of chicken crates, stacked ready for catching the next morning, and which Paul had failed to notice. But we had the building where we wanted it, and the driver and his mate, with the help of that labour-saving invention, the lorry crane, had it stacked on the ground in no time. Loaded or unloaded, it never ceases to surprise me how small a space is occupied by the component parts of a building which, when erected, will cover a vast area.

The erectors were another matter. These gangs of men, usually in my experience cheerful, adaptable, talented and quick at their job, have also one great failing. When you want them on your site, they are invariably engaged on another, usually at the other end of the country and difficult to contact even by their own HQ. The nettles and grass grow up round the piled asbestos, the steel stanchions begin their long journey into rust, the bags of nuts and bolts split and spill, and the phone grows hot with increasingly repetitive promises.

To add insult to injury the cattle got out one night, and for eight uninhibited hours used our building site as their play-ground, having a particularly jolly time with the remains of the fires, which these usually docile castrates head-butted and pawed as though they were rampant bulls. Only when all hope had almost been abandoned did we see the welcome sight of a large van towing a battered caravan coming up our lane, and out jumped just two men. Yes, we were promised four, but one had the flu and the other had gone to an aunt's funeral.

These two worthies surveyed the site with critical eyes, remarked that the levels did not look too good, and asked why the digger was not there. Paul informed them that it came the day before, waited all morning, then went away. The foreman borrowed our phone (for the first of many times), rang up his boss somewhere in the Outer Hebrides, then the plant hire company, then cheerfully told us that no way could the digger be back on site until the next morning. He and his mate did a bit of juggling with strings and sticks, marked out the site, then disappeared to the pub.

Next day, miracle of miracles, not only did the digger arrive on time to dig out holes for the stanchions (we also got him to tidy up the gateway), but the concrete arrived to fill the holes in after, rather than before, they were actually dug. The skeleton of The New Piggery started to take shape, always an exciting sight, and we were hopeful that flesh would soon be put on these bones. Our hopes were dashed when the three men, one having returned from his wake looking decidedly the worse for wear, announced they were off to finish another job while the concrete set. However, having started, they were just as anxious as we were to finish the job, and, good as their word, were back next day. With impressive speed, interrupted

67

only briefly to sup tea, they began to erect the frame for the cladding.

We now felt that we could begin to chivvy our next sub-contractor, whose job I will explain. In our great wisdom, and for some extraordinary reason imagining that we knew best – when most of our previous experience should have taught us that we badly needed expert guidance – we had decided upon a fattening house which was designed to be a sophisticated spin-off from my own large, enclosed pig yards. After all our pipeline/slurry dramas at The Piggery, Paul had become attracted to the uncomplicated system on my own unit. Needless to say, it was anathema to pig specialists, but it suited me.

So we planned our new building to provide small yards to house fifty to sixty pigs, ad-lib fed with the feed hoppers forming the front partition of the pens. To enable us to clean out these yards easily with a tractor and loader there were to be large doors along one side of the building, each one giving access to a yard. As with my system, the pigs would lie on straw or shavings, so the litter would be easily handled by conventional dung spreaders. It was the doors to the yards we now had to get made and fitted. And what a performance that turned out to be.

The large steel doors for our new piggery were to be made by a firm run by a great character from Paul's industrial past, a dynamic French-Tunisian East Ender called Joe. His surname was more complicated, but was corrupted by his friends into 'Kamikaze' after his driving technique. For a preliminary survey and an amused look at what his old mate was up to on a pig farm of all places, Joe drove down from London in his red Porsche. When Paul had first met Joe he drove a large Mercedes. Following a cash-flow crisis he had traded down to a clapped-out van, but rapidly revived to his present impressive runabout.

This Porsche looked out of place amid the mud and confusion of our site, which heavy rain was turning into a no-go area. In his snappy suit Joe looked equally at odds with his surround-ings; like many Londoners he appeared surprised that the countryside was not all decently tarmacadamed. He stepped delicately from his car, advanced a few muddy yards to meet us, then bent down to clean his mocassins. Good-humouredly he tiptoed around with Paul taking measurements, wondering aloud why Paul could have been so foolish as to swap his warm office for such conditions. After a cup of coffee in what was to be Paul's new home, Joe disappeared up our road from a Brands Hatch start to galvanise his small factory into action on our behalf (he said).

Much to our later regret we had settled on steel doors, partly because Joe quoted a price cheaper than that received for wooden ones, and partly because Paul had faith in Joe and his expertise. To give Joe his due, he had misgivings when he actually saw the project, but airily brushed them aside. I was really the person who should have appreciated what effect the atmosphere inside our building would have on steel, but mistakenly I imagined that the improved ventilation we had installed would cope with any problem. When they eventually arrived the doors were even heavier and less manageable than we had envisaged, and it took the combined efforts of three of Joe's cockney workforce to get them onto their hinges.

As you can imagine these workers were absolutely fascinated by the farm, especially by the chicks in our broiler houses. Propaganda had obviously led them to expect caged misery, and they were most impressed to see the chicks happy and lively in their controlled environment. As a PR exercise I always make a point of showing non-farming visitors our chicken unit. Their pleased reaction, 'I had no idea it was like this,' emphasises just how ignorant many of our town cousins are of the practicalities of farming today.

There was a great deal of pulling and pushing, heaving and straining, and 'right said Fred-ing' before the doors were up, and one near escape from disaster when one of the fifteen-foot by ten-foot monsters which was propped against the lorry blew over in a fierce gust of wind and missed making a nasty mess of Paul's English collie by inches. Frightened out of its skin the poor brute yelled piteously and disappeared into the wood at great speed with its tail between its legs, refusing to return for two days until it was satisfied the coast was clear.

When the doors were eventually in position, it was quite obvious that, in spite of their apparent solidity, because of their great weight they were going to sag on their hinges. Joe, who had arrived on site dressed this time in fur-lined anorak, Cossack hat and new green wellingtons (with straps) scratched his head, did some quick calculations on the back of an envelope – which I suspect involved the 3.30 at Brighton – and shot off to prepare a solution.

This solution consisted of an ingenious device welded from one corner to another on each door, with a large nut at one end to take up any slack once the door had settled in position. It did not work. Then we tried slides for the doors to rest on and open on. These jammed on the new concrete and did not live up to their name. Finally, we settled for small wheels. These worked well for a time until the shafts rusted and the wheels refused to turn; so opening each door became a tedious leverage with crowbar and shovel. These doors had a nil insulation value, and were soon rusting most dramatically. The best we could say of them was that they served an expensive purpose. But it was fun to meet Joe, who, to pay his men, to our great envy produced the largest roll of soiled banknotes we had ever seen.

Meanwhile, the rest of the world moved on apace. The three erectors (the fourth never did turn up) had finished their task, apart from fixing the guttering, which had been forgotten, and had departed leaving us with a steel shell, roofed, and clad down the sides to the projected height of a wall. This wall was designed to be strong enough to contain the pigs, and to withstand the pressure of the tractor and loader when cleaning out. November, having given up an unequal struggle with the elements, gave way to December. It rained, and it blew, then it froze. We were struggling to finish the concreting. (More – much more – of that later.) At the same time Paul was still running The Piggery, some ten miles away, and also trying to prepare his new quarters for habitation. As a builder and decorator, Paul was an unusual mixture of the string-and-tie brigade and the perfectionist. He was determined that his bungalow, at least, would be pristine bright and ready for occupation on time.

At The Piggery the situation was deteriorating. As we emptied the pens the building came colder and the remaining inhabitants suffered from pneumonia and dysentery either alternately or both together. We had also to clean out the place as we went along, to leave it all neat and tidy, and had a number of minor repairs to complete under the beady eye of our landlord's wife, who I do not think had ever forgiven us for

70

laughing when she drove her new car through the slurry overflow.

Then Paul, still seeking DIY perfection at the bungalow, managed to drill through the new wiring he had installed and just plastered over. We felt that perhaps fate was not on our side. We sat down in his bare, cold kitchen to take stock. Even with the extended deadline our landlord had granted us it was obvious we were not going to get the site clear by that time, for slow growth rates and a poor trade were making a nonsense of our predictions. (Not for the first time.) We were going to be left with a number of pigs too small for sale.

We also had a number of sows at The Piggery to which Paul had become attached, and which he was keen to bring over to The New Piggery as the foundation of our herd, and several of these would have litters at foot. So we decided to make the best of a bad job and transport all the remaining stock from one site to another as soon as The New Piggery was ready, and pray that we did not transport too many of the problems we had been anxious to leave behind us. This decision, which was forced on us, has a strong claim, against fierce competition, to be one of the worst we made in our chequered career.

Chapter Eight

'How are you?' said Winnie the Pooh. Eeyore shook his head from side to side.
'Not very how,' he said. 'I don't seem to have felt at all how for a long time.'

As MANY hopeful pig empire builders will be all too aware, it is the concreting of a new site which takes most time and effort. We were faced with the concreting of about an acre of what is often described in the advisory press as a 'green field site'. Whatever its beginnings – and ours, you will remember, was a blasted forest – in no time at all it becomes a morass of mud, ruts and inconvenience.

Now, concreting is all very easy if you have lots of money and can employ a specialist firm – assuming you can find one you can rely upon – who move in with the right machine to level the site; who cart in loads of decent hardcore which is carefully laid and then rolled and topped with small stone; who have proper retaining metal partitions with slots and pins to hold them firm; who, when the site is levelled and properly set out with spirit levels and string and other aids to modern technology, then have ready-mixed concrete delivered and shot in the right place. Finally, this concrete is smoothed and coaxed into a shiny new surface with tamping boards, which, wonder of wonders, even have little motors on them to make them vibrate. (I could do with one of those attached to me at times.)

Needless to say, our concreting operation bore no resemblance to this professional job. For one thing, we had no money. We cajoled our neighbour into one final fling with his ancient and wheezy Drott to scrape the site, which, when he had finished, looked like a lunar landscape. Our hardcore was unwanted gleanings from building sites, dumped over the years at the farm by the in-laws' firm. It consisted of a mixture of rubble, lumps of brickwork, large pieces of concrete with metal rods sticking out of them, broken glass, lavatory pans and guttering, and empty fruit pie cartons. This had to be painfully broken into reasonable size (by hand) to make the semblance of a base. The craters and valleys of this base would be roughly levelled by in-filling with ballast hastily snatched from the heap by the mixer, in between the deliveries of barrowloads of wet concrete.

Our shuttering boards were of equal vintage and origin, warped and twisted timbers from demolished vicarages and schools – the in-laws specialise in the educational end of the market – which had to be juggled to produce a nearly straight edge. They were kept in place by wooden stakes and lumps of concrete, and periodically collapsed outwards from the weight of the too-wet concrete. (Too wet because it is easier to spread that way. And yes. I do know that is meant to bring the cement to the top and weaken the mixture. But speed was of the essence.)

As I have never been convinced by the argument that ready-mix concrete is finally as cheap as materials purchased and mixed on site, we determined to mix all the concrete ourselves. To this end we bought a tractor-mounted mixer ('sure to be useful in the future'), the exposed chain of which continually jammed with wet concrete, and which our long-in-the-tooth Fordson could not raise high enough for easy emptying. As a consequence, I continually found my own relatively modern tractor missing when I wanted it, to be discovered on Paul's site throbbing away with the mixer attached. 'Thought you'd gone out,' Paul would explain with a guilty grin.

As for labour, well, to start with, Paul managed to convince some of his old mates, a few of whom we have already met, that a few hours shovelling ballast and cement would not only help him, but prove beneficial to their health. It was interesting and instructive to see their initial enthusiasm evaporate as the area of concrete completed oh-so-painfully and oh-so-slowly crept over the site. After some days the excuses became so frequent that it was difficult to raise a gang.

I shall never forget the look of relief on our publican friend's face when he had the opportunity to escape sweated labour for an hour or so in order to rush me into hospital after an auger sliced off the top of one of my fingers. I suffered this mutilation when I stupidly checked, manually, to feel if the slide of a new auger we had just had installed was correctly adjusted. Too late I discovered it was not.

73

'It's an ill wind,' Alan philosophically remarked as he slid behind the driving wheel beside me, I holding my bloody digit in the air, having looked and failed to find the severed part in the pig meal. Lots of nasty jokes about next week's pork pies.

'I'll wait for you,' he said cheerfully at the hospital, balancing a welcome cup of tea on his lap and eyeing the passing nurses. After a lady doctor had tut-tutted over my finger and asked my permission, I had quite a gang of these lovelies around me as I lay on the table, viewing the chipping away of my finger bone with professional interest; which certainly helped to dull the pain and stiffen my lip.

'Make a neat job of it,' I said to the doctor as she expertly wielded needle and thread. 'I've got to live with it the rest of my life.'

'Well, you shouldn't have been so ruddy careless,' was the sharp reply. The lovelies giggled. By the time Alan had taxied me back to the farm, the anaesthetic was wearing off and I was not feeling at all chatty.

As Paul was still belting backwards and forwards to The Piggery twice a day, where our remaining pigs huddled in miserable groups in the few occupied pens in the cavernous building, he was rarely on site at The New Piggery to supervise and encourage, though his recently retired father proved a gallant stand-in. Work got further and further behind schedule, the weather deteriorated from rain and sleet to frost and snow. The changeover date (January 1st, extended to January 31st) came nearer and nearer.

Then, to our relief, arrived an old friend from Canada, where he was engaged upon building his own log house on a plot he had acquired years previously as a reward for his labours. As the snow was presently ten foot deep in his part of Canada he had returned home for a visit, and was looking for some work to pay his return fare. Russell was of a gentle, philosophical disposition, and with his flowing locks reminded me of the pictures of Jesus in primary school textbooks. Although we could have done with any number of miracles we settled for more worldly benefits, and quickly agreed to his suggestion that he completed the concreting for what was a very reasonable price.

He soon rounded up a gang of disciples, one or two of whom we rather disconcertingly discovered had done what is colloquially known as 'time'. Rehabilitation was obviously one of the enthusiasms of Russell's missionary nature, believing as he did that love and brotherly co-operation make the world go round. (Foolish youth!) However, his gang turned out to be jovial, hard-working, hard-drinking, hard-swearing characters, rough on machinery and careless with tools – particularly other people's – but who set to with a will under Russell's quiet control. He never seemed to mind clearing up after them, and to our enormous relief the concreting proceeded apace.

With Russell and his gang busily engaged upon what the Probation Service refer to as 'after-care', we were now able to concentrate upon preparing the building itself for the migrants from The Piggery, presently shoving off from those shores on a sea of overflowing slurry. The completed shell of The New Piggery now loomed majestically above and beyond the three lower, leaner chicken sheds, which fortunately shielded from the road much of the chaos surrounding it. Considering the noise and the mess we were making, it was just as well that the chicken unit was empty and between batches.

With the agreement of these tenants we arranged to connect water and electricity from the nearest chicken shed to The New Piggery. By a miracle of planning and foresight, we actually remembered to dig the necessary trenches before, rather than after, the labour gang concreted over the route. One of these trenches ran for some yards alongside the existing concrete road. Our neighbour with the dyspeptic Drott had dug and then filled this in, leaving as is usual a mound of earth above the line, which he recommended us to level off in due time by running the wheel of a tractor along it.

Unfortunately, one of the gang anticipated this instruction before the trench had a chance to settle. While moving Paul's ancient Fordson, Old Nellie herself, he carelessly left the edge of the concrete and finished up with one wheel of the tractor almost as deep as the buried water pipe. The tractor itself rested upon its belly at an acute angle. The apologetic admission by the offender that he had over-indulged the night before and was not seeing too well that morning was no consolation at all as we manoeuvred with planks of wood, jacks and (eventually when all else had failed) a borrowed four-wheel drive tractor to remove Old Nellie from her entrenched position.

After numerous and frustrating efforts during which Old Nellie merely moved a few inches along the muddy trench before subsiding once more with a gasp of exhaustion, we finally constructed a raft of wood and concrete posts beneath her front and rear wheels. She seemed to regard this operation as an assault upon her old-maid's chastity, rather than a rescue act, and resisted strenuously. The raft was designed to support the sunken wheel as it emerged from the mire. With great shouting, heaving, revving of engines and slipping of clutches, Old Nellie slowly and, oh so painfully, her wheels spinning, her tummy rumbling, her gallant engine coughing and farting and spewing black smoke and burning smuts over us all, at long last persuaded her rear wheel to climb onto the makeshift raft.

A great cheer rang out, drowned by my panic-stricken scream of 'WhoooaaaaaAAAAA', as the towing tractor driver nearly continued too far and pulled Nell off the raft and back into the trench, where the front wheel was still held fast. He slapped on his brakes just in time, and the tow-rope slackened and subsided in the mud. Having got so far, it was relatively easy to jack up the front of the tractor, place boards under the front and rear wheels and pull Old Nellie to the safe shore of the concrete road. The poor old thing seemed to shake herself like a dog, and to ask plaintively why she should be subjected to such indignities at her advanced age. Why indeed! The chicken unit manager arrived for the last acts of this drama. As he surveyed the mess of mud, skid-marks and oil on his concrete road, and the excited participants, all appearing to do different things at different times, and all loudly shouting contradictory instructions, he must have wondered what sort of neighbours he had acquired. I took him off for a cup of coffee, while Paul and the gang cleared up and gave Old Nell a hospital check-up.

The only consolation to this drama was that the water-pipe in the trench appeared to be undamaged. We had been hopeful that once the connection had been made, the tenants would forget that we were drawing from their supply and we might get our water free. But they were too wise to be caught by an old dodge like that, hard as we might lie that our usage would be minimal. Every quarter we received a complicated account, detailing the excess water used over their normal consumption. As is the fashion with modern companies, they are great ones for statistics, computers, etc., which spew out endless demands, invoices and statements. And yes, I know we should have had a meter, but for some reason I cannot recall, we did not have one. The only water we did get away with was from the outside tap common to us both. And we nearly lost that facility when, on a surprise visit, the area manager caught Paul washing his van there.

Perhaps as a divine judgement for our dishonest greed, one frosty night a stand-in for the local manager, on a tour of inspection, turned off our stop-cock, not realising what its significance was. As a result, Paul had a right panic the next morning – we had by then pigs in The New Piggery – as with dread memory he assumed he was frozen up. He spent much valuable time trying vainly to thaw out empty pipes before he cottoned on to what had happened.

With water and electricity connected, we were able to push on with the internal work. Our bricklayer – another Paul relation – was a sturdy but diminutive person, and he had a mighty struggle with the solid concrete blocks which we had acquired cheaply (surplus from another job) and which we were using for the pen divisions. By the time he had lifted a goodly number of these to the full five-foot height of the walls David was wearing a particularly pained expression. Certainly the tempo of slip/slash as he trowelled the sand and cement became progressively slower. It was early afternoon when he declared that the light was too poor to continue, and our offer of a lead light was rejected.

The next day David returned with a mate. This underling was given the task of handing the blocks up to David as he stood on his raised platform trowelling away and impatiently awaiting the next block as his mate staggered from heap to wall, the blocks quite obviously becoming heavier and heavier as the day wore on. It reminded me of those far-away threshing-tackle days when the 2¼ cwt (oh, very well, 114 kg) sacks of wheat always seemed to have to be carried up steep steps to the granary. Those nostalgic for the 'good old days' would soon lose their enthusiasm if subjected to the sweated labour of a few days with a threshing tackle, amid the itching dirt and dust. How we used to pray for that long, slapping drive belt to come off the pulleys and give us a brief respite!

I hasten to add that I was only a slip of a lad, on school holiday and on the periphery of these throbbing events – chaff boy usually – who used to look forward with sadistic glee to the rat hunt which accompanied the finish of each stack. If a stack was not finished by the end of the day, a wire netting fence would be temporarily erected around it, so the rats could not escape overnight. I suppose today there would be a Society for the Preservation of the Farmyard Rat (SPFR)!

Meanwhile, back at The New Piggery Russell was having trouble with his gang, whose initial enthusiasm was wearing off fast. I think the forced labour may have reminded at least one of these characters rather too vividly of his recent past, and the joint attractions of lazy mornings in bed and social security benefits proved too tempting to withstand for long. Another was showing all-too-obvious signs of incipient alcoholism, and complained that his head throbbed in unison with the mixer. A stand-in, who joined because he had fallen out with his live-in girlfriend, patched up the quarrel in double-quick time after a day spent in the company of a shovel.

However, Russell accepted such setbacks with his usual philosophical calm. With his long, thick black hair tied in a pony-tail with ribbon, his knotted bandana, his ragged, patched jeans, his worn leather jacket, his jovial face wreathed in several days' stubble and a shy smile, he was a startling sight for our more conventional visitors. They were even more disconcerted by his quiet, cultured voice and his air of calm assurance as he would pause to speak to us from his energetic shovelling of ballast and cement into our by now very worn and battered mixer. But, whatever his appearance, Russell never had any problem at all attracting members of the opposite sex, who seemed to regard him as a sort of guru (which, of course, he was). These young ladies were only too pleased to labour all day for Russell, and it aroused our envy to see the tough little favourite of one day replaced by an identikit version the next. We just had to take care to get the name right.

Russell was helped on occasions by his artist brother-in-law, all flowing locks and earrings, but also a successful amateur builder, having converted a tithe barn to a home of great originality. He shared Russell's idealistic belief that the world

78

could, and should, be a place of gentle harmony, if we but loved our neighbour and stopped exploiting each other and the animal kingdom. As one would expect, both Russell and Richard were vegetarians, and they had to overcome considerable misgivings even to work outside on such an establishment as ours. (Money had something to do with it.) I think they were puzzled by the apparent contradiction that although Paul, and probably also myself, seemed to be kindly and reasonable human beings, we saw nothing wrong with rearing animals in intensive conditions for slaughter and human consumption. Paul, for instance, when not greedily consuming a mixed grill, was often to be seen photographing birds, fondling his dog (who did not deserve it), or otherwise communing with nature. Even I had been observed giving a sow a friendly pat on her rump, and speaking quite kindly to my children.

Russell would have his lunch with Paul, which Paul would cook. Russell had no objection to eating eggs, which comprised Paul's staple diet at this time, the pullets in the chicken unit having helpfully started to lay before they departed to their finishing schools. Russell was not impressed by my (untruthful) reprimand that he was depriving a dear little chick of life and liberty, but he did insist that his eggs were cooked in a pan well cleansed of any residue of meat. Paul, whose temporary bachelor existence was not perhaps noted for its domestic tidiness, always assured Russell that the pan had been thoroughly washed, even when this might not have been strictly true. Russell eventually became suspicious of the hamburger-flavoured omelettes, and from then on brought his own sandwiches, wholemeal bread bulging with nutritious, naturally grown greenery, washed down with goat's yoghurt from the foothills of the Bavarian mountains. (At least, that is what the container claimed.)

I regret that one traumatic incident did little to convert Russell or Richard to the joys of intensive farming. One of the chicken sheds adjacent to The New Piggery had to be cleared of birds in a hurry, and there was a great shortage of labour for catching. Russell and Richard who were working on site were somehow cajoled by Paul to lend a hand. Mind you, by this time almost anything was a welcome relief from shovelling into the mixer, barrowing wet concrete, and producing a level surface for the dog to tread on. Unfortunately, as Russell entered the darkened shed, he inadvertently trod on the legs of a chicken and his boot pinioned it to the floor. As he followed through with his other leg, the metal cap of his boot decapitated the poor brute.

I do not think anyone who was there will ever forget the look of utter horror on Russell's face as he realized what he had done. How Russell managed to continue catching chickens I shall never know. Perhaps he reasoned that every penny he earned would take him that much quicker away from our meaty empire and back to the snowy wastes of Vancouver.

Although our building progress was about three months behind schedule, we had by now more than over-stayed our welcome at The Piggery, and felt we could not ask our obliging landlord for any further extensions. Indeed, with our commuting difficulties we were quite as anxious to vacate the premises as his wife was to see us go. To do this in an organised and efficient way – a course, readers will realise, somewhat foreign to our nature – took a deal of planning. For, having reluctantly decided to transfer what pigs were left in The Piggery, we had to move not only the livestock, but also the mill-and-mixer and sundry other items of essential equipment. The mill-and-mixer had to be wired up and working on the new site on the same day as the transfer to enable us to continue feeding the same rations. To save continual to-ing and fro-ing, the Big Plan was to move everything at once, mustering as much help as we estimated we would need or could afford.

At The New Piggery we had managed to get two pens ready for the invasion. One of these was left twice the planned eventual size, to accommodate all the store pigs we were transferring. The other was to house temporarily those few sows and piglets which we had left and could not sell. For although Paul had managed to demonstrate that he had the right midwifery instincts and a penchant for dealing with awkward females, initially we now intended to concentrate on fattening at The New Piggery. The urgent necessity to generate a cash flow in the muddy waters of our finances had forced us to abandon for the time being Paul's ambitious plans to start a breeding herd, using his favourite porcine models from The Piggery. What we were left with were the sows with unweaned piglets, and one or two others needing a quiet convalescence to put flesh on old bones to make them even half-presentable.

The great day dawned bright and cold. From far and wide men and machines descended upon The Piggery. Friend and adviser Des in deepest Suffolk started, or rather, attempted to start, a borrowed lorry to transport the mill-and-mixer. From Somerset, another lorry set out to collect the redundant whey tank. From Bedfordshire trundled from its stable an ancient crane. From Hertfordshire our faithful haulier sent two of his floats and two of his best-natured drivers. From The New Piggery went Peter and Paul in two vans. From pubs and clubs, bed-sitters, marital and non-marital couches came many characters to 'lend a hand'. And if, gentle reader, you think all this activity a recipe for disaster, I am afraid that you are right!

This eccentric collection of humans and vehicles was speeding towards The Piggery from far and wide with the worthy objective of moving both machinery and animals to The New Piggery in one concerted, well-timed effort. It was essential to our plan that not only all the vehicles, but also most (if not all) of our volunteer helpers arrived on site more or less together to help with the loading of the mill-and-mixer, the whey tank, some assorted fixtures and fittings, the sows and piglets, and the store pigs. We had mustered our rather care-worn group of vehicles and men – the ladies forgot about Women's Lib and sensibly stopped at home with the dishes – as a measure of economy. Anyone who has attempted to hire modern heavy tackle will appreciate why. Unfortunately, as with so many frugalities, this one turned out to be a somewhat false economy.

The first hitch was that, in his part of deepest Suffolk, Des was unable to start his borrowed lorry, which admittedly had seen better days, and had not appreciated being left out overnight in the dark and cold in Des's yard. When he eventually managed to tow the stubborn brute into life, he then discovered that it was low on fuel, and had to make a time-consuming detour to fill up. Meanwhile, his wife was trying to contact one of us on the telephone to warn us of Des's late arrival. We, of course, were heading east into the rising sun toward The Piggery. At last my wife managed to relay a message to us via the couple who lived in the farmhouse at The Piggery. They were interested spectators at our preparations for departure, probably reflecting that their assorted livestock would be able to glean uninterrupted from now on, and that the smell and the slurry problem might diminish. (They were wrong on both counts.)

This initial hiccup, plus the non-arrival of the crane, threw all our well-laid plans awry. Still, the cattle floats had arrived on time, so we decided to load the pigs first and send them on ahead accompanied by one of us to help unload in the right place. For even if Russell or any of his gang had been at The New Piggery to help unload, it was too much to expect them to recognise the temporary bed and breakfast arrangements for our stock. As it turned out, they were not there, but still snuggled up in their own dorms. I rapidly volunteered to go with the cattle lorries, sensing it might be the best option.

We backed one of the floats as close as possible to the rickety door of the shed where our few remaining sows and their litters dwelt in a line of pens fronting a large open area, with the door in the middle. Now, any of you who have attempted to load pigs (or any livestock) from an open space onto a confined lorry will appreciate the difficulties we faced. These were accentuated by the dashing around of frenzied sows searching for their young, which we had just carried squealing hideously onto the lorry, and the sprinting about of the stronger of the piglets once they found their feet and their unusual freedom.

As their mums were pulled, pushed and exhorted up the ramp, they would be passed by their litters going down. These latter would do a couple of quick circuits of the building before dashing up the ramp once again – rather like lambs at play – just as their mother had managed to force four sweating and swearing humans to allow her to return to ground level, where she set out in search of her missing young.

We tried penning the piglets at the front of the lorry, but the smallest squeezed through the bars and escaped once more. By now the crescendo of noise was such that we were later told that the pupils in the local school some mile or so across the open fields had difficulty hearing their teacher, who was appropriately reading them an extract from *Pinky and Perky Go Shopping*. Then we rigged up solid barriers at the front of the lorry, behind which we penned the piglets. This further distracted the mums, who could now hear but could not see their progeny, and who were by now totally confused by the whole operation. One or two of the sows just gave up in disgust and lay down, having completely lost interest in a family which could lead them such a dance.

As an encore, one of the more active gilts burst through the gap between the lorry and the building, taking a section of the lorry tail-gate with it, and headed for the smaller of the slurry pits, where she enjoyed a cooling dip. By the time we had got her to shore and back to the building we were all generously covered in splashes of stinking slurry from her heaving flanks; I had stubbed a toe when I foolishly aimed a kick at her and missed; while the helpful good humour of the drivers was diminishing every pulsating minute.

If only grown pigs realised their strength it would be impossible to load them on to any lorry if they decided they did not want to go. They just have to lie down and refuse to move. There have been a number of times in my long career loading pigs when I have put my head in my hands, leant against the wall, listened to my pounding heart, and been prepared to give up. Only the determination, better physique and more placid temper of my helpers has persuaded me to persevere, and we have always, somehow, sometime, managed to load the awkward brutes eventually. I always think of occasions like these when animal-loving visitors ask: 'Aren't you sorry to see them go?'

'No,' I reply firmly. 'Just the reverse.'

This was one of those occasions. If it had not been for the jolly face of Des, who had just arrived with his lorry ('Going like a bomb'), and the rejuvenation a fresh helper always produces, with his cheerful, 'Hallo, having a bit of trouble?' plus the extra pair of hands, I think at least I would have been defeated. Instead, as so often happens, it was the pigs who decided that enough was enough and followed the slurry gilt up the ramp, holding their noses delicately up in the air. With a friendly smack on her rump from Des the last sow trotted on to the lorry as though she could not understand what all the fuss was about, and the ramp was hastily and thankfully slammed shut before she could change her mind.

After all that, loading the store pigs from the main building on to the other lorry was easy. For one thing, we had a proper

loading ramp and a narrow alleyway to drive them along to
reach it. As these remaining store pigs were all to go into one
pen at The New Piggery, we let them out from their various
pens into the alleyway all together so they could get well and
truly mixed up. The resulting seething cauldron of fighting,
woofing, screaming and galloping pigs was slowly eased towards
the lorry, with us giving ground occasionally to improve the
mix. All the combatants in the porcine equivalent of a battle
royal between rival gangs of football supporters quickly became
smothered in lookalike slime, their beady eyes glinting out of the
grey background, as they slithered and fought their way along
the greasy alleyway policed by us. By the time we had them on
the lorry they would have had difficulty in recognising their
nearest and dearest, let alone any potential enemy.

With great relief I clambered up beside one of the drivers for
our journey to The New Piggery. I have a childlike pleasure in
sitting perched up high in the cab of a lorry, able to see over
hedges and into the front rooms of houses, where interesting
vistas are sometimes to be glimpsed. It is also satisfying for a
change not to be one of the long line of impatient vehicles
queued up behind, waiting for that short stretch of straight road
to overtake with an angry roar of acceleration.

As we drove splash splash down the drive we met the crane
just arriving. And that deserves a new chapter.

Chapter Nine

'And whether pigs have wings.' (L. Carroll)

THE CRANE driver turned out to be one of those sad souls to whom life appears to be a constant burden. I suppose having to manipulate a vehicle which had arrived on The Ark had soured him. Perhaps, poor man, he also had a nagging wife, two glue-sniffing teenagers, and a mother-in-law who constantly told him to 'cheer up, things could be worse'. To add to his woes, he had crossed the frontier from Bedfordshire some hours earlier, having cleared customs, and had then got utterly lost among the narrow lanes of rural Herts.

Having at long last located The Piggery, he was confronted by two large cattle floats full of squealing pigs who were obviously not going to give way to a mere crane – our drivers were feeling pretty bolshy by this time – and he had to back up a quarter of a mile of narrow track to let them through. When, going backwards, he slipped off the side of the gravel track and on to our landlord's winter wheat we feared the worst. But with much grating of gears, churning of wheels (and wheat) and revving of engine he managed to regain firm ground, and continue backwards to a passing point. With a cheery wave we swept by him, leaving him to slosh through the slurry for the first time.

So when he eventually drove into the farmyard and found a noisy group of filthy, sweaty people all drinking tea out of thermos flasks, one of whom, Paul, greeted him with: 'And where have you been mate?' he was not in the best of tempers. To give Paul his due, he quickly summed up the situation and set about placating the driver by offering him both tea and sympathy, and a humorous account of the morning so far. This would have sounded more amusing had there not been still a lot left to do. Co-operation was sorely needed for the rest of the enterprise. However, now all were on site, the natural good humour of Paul and his mates began to surface, and they were beginning to 'wind up' each other, as the descriptive phrase has it.

One or two late arrivals – Alan, for instance, 'Quite a night at the hostelry last night, old boy,' as he lit one fag from the stub of another, his hand shaking feverishly – had missed the exhausting trauma of loading the pigs, and were relatively fresh for the fray. They were actually looking forward to the job of moving and loading the mill-and-mixer, the whey tank, and other impedimenta. Even the normally quiet and retiring Brian clapped his hands together with apparent enthusiasm, and said, 'Let's get on with it then,' impatient to return to his cosy lab and more gentle pursuits. The answers he provoked were both unprintable and ambiguous.

Still, time was pressing and there was much to do. Because of the hiccup, the first inhabitants of The New Piggery would be moving in before the furniture arrived. Not possessing the initiative of Orwell's 1984 group, they were unlikely to be able to cope on their own. The electrician, who had arrived at The Piggery in time to observe with wide-eyed wonder the loading antics, had by now disconnected the mill-and-mixer, and was to be at The New Piggery after lunch to reconnect it there, and to carry out other essential wiring duties. As it was not possible to get the crane into the building, the mill-and-mixer had got to be manhandled outside for loading. But first the various pipes had to be hammered apart, having rusted solid.

'So that's why it's been so slow grinding recently,' remarked Paul as he removed a dead rat from inside one of them. Then the mixer, followed by the mill, was pushed, pulled and rolled over some yards of concrete towards the crane. Meanwhile, Des was manoeuvring his non-power-assisted-steering, engine-spluttering lorry with some difficulty on the slippery forecourt into a convenient position to receive the mill-and-mixer from the crane.

Still looking disgruntled, and completely unamused by the various suggestions as to overnight indulgences made among the gang as they laboriously shunted the mill-and-mixer into position, the crane driver supervised the attaching of ropes and chains and hooks on to the mixer. The centre of balance was, of course, quite wrong, and as the mixer left the ground it swept Alan, who was lighting yet another coffin nail, off his feet and into the mud, to the glee of his friends. The look he gave them as he got up did not hold out much promise of drinks on the house the next time they called in to prop up his bar. The ropes were readjusted, and the mixer swayed up and towards Des's lorry, which seemed to tremble at the sight.

With good reason. Either the ropes were too long, or the crane jib too short, with the result that the bottom of the mixer was some six inches below the side of the flat back of the lorry. As it gyrated beside it the mixer gave the lorry a very nasty shove, which would have brought it a red card on the football field, shifting the lorry several inches sideways. After yet more adjustments to ropes and chains, the crane driver next time managed to hoist the mixer over the rear of Des's lorry, but either from spite or incompetence lowered it far too abruptly. The lorry gave a sigh of pain, the floorboards cracked ominously, and the leaf springs flattened through their greasy rust. Diplomatically, the gang stayed silent. It was probably an optical illusion that the lorry appeared to have a sag in the middle, but just in case it was not, Paul and others jumped up and man-handled the mixer to the front, to alter the centre of balance, not liking to trust the crane driver with too delicate a manoeuvre.

This left room for the mill unit, which went on with little fuss. It is surprising how quickly one learns, and the ropes were attached and the mill lifted with a measure of expertise. Perhaps ashamed, the crane driver deposited this lighter burden quite delicately behind its mate, to whom it snuggled up affectionately. However, neither section of the mill-and-mixer looked particularly safe and sound. Paul left Des to busy himself roping up his ungainly load, while the others turned their attention to the whey tank.

The whey tank had proved pretty obstreperous when we had initially received it, threatening, if you recall, to flatten parts of The Piggery by swinging itself about rather like one of those huge metal balls which gives so much spectator value on demolition sites. This time all went fairly well. For one thing, the collecting lorry had its own crane and an experienced operator. But first the tank had to be moved outside.

This was effected by a combination of ancient crane (to pull), scaffold pipes (to roll), a tractor with a front-loader (to push), and brute strength leavened with nervous caution. The difficulty was to co-ordinate the efforts of these various aids, not to mention the danger of crushing one or two of the less nimble helpers against the wall when the pushing or pulling became too enthusiastic, and the tank slipped yet again off the rollers and scarred the concrete. However, by climbing on a wall and shouting instructions above the din of machinery and excited voices, Paul managed the operation successfully, and the tank was then hoisted upon its lorry with no fuss at all by the driver, who even produced a slight smile, combined with a look of quiet superiority aimed at the other driver. The lads looked pleased, and pretended not to notice.

Paul had now to load up various smaller pieces of machinery, bags of meal and so on; then to look around, scratch his head and wonder if he had forgotten anything. The Piggery looked strangely deserted and silent, and rather sad. As with any move, memories of the good and bad times came flooding back. Fortunately, the fun and the small successes outweighed the bleaker disappointments. The Piggery symbolised for us our joint venture, a great deal of enthusiasm and hard work. But this was no time for nostalgia. With a shout of 'Let 'em roll' (Paul had been watching an old John Wayne movie), the convoy, headed by Two-Gun Des and his swaying load, drove through the slurry and down the drive for the last time.

At the door of the farmhouse stood the couple with whom Paul had enjoyed a somewhat uneasy relationship. I had always found them friendly and helpful, and good for cups of coffee and chats, but I suspected they found Paul's happy-go-lucky, rather casual approach to the (too) many problems associated with the large and smelly pig unit sited on their doorstep somewhat trying at times. Like getting rid of a not quite satisfactory neighbour to your trim semi-detached in leafy suburbia, feelings of relief were probably mixed with some apprehension as to who would arrive on your doorstep next. I regret that our landlords had made no efforts to persuade us to stay, so either we had not been their ideal as tenants, or they had someone better in view. (It turned out to be the former, though they achieved the latter.)

Today, however, it was all smiles and waves as the convoy

consisting of Des's lorry, lurching dangerously under the weight of the mill-and-mixer; the crane, with an only slightly mollified driver; the whey tank lorry; our ancient (and illegal – no handbrake, no cab, no mirrors, etc.) tractor and trailer (equally illegal), loaded with what looked like the left-overs from a farm sale; plus a variety of cars, vans and motor bikes, chundered by and headed for the open road. A meeting of battalion HQ had decided it was safer to travel together, in case any of the component parts of the convoy suffered a breakdown. By the sound of Des's lorry this threatened to occur before it had even reached the road. But with two mighty backfires and an impressive emission of black smoke it turned successfully out of the farm drive and set off in pursuit of the two cattle floats.

At The New Piggery, where a lot of the action was now to take place, the state of play was as follows. All our remaining pigs, comprising some dozen sows and litters, and about 130 store pigs, and all our fixtures and fittings, had now been cleared from The Piggery and were en route to The New Piggery which was far from ready. Like the buyers of new houses who have to move in while the plaster is still wet and the 'landscaping' just a pretty picture on the advertising literature we were relieved to be moving at last into our own place. (Give or take some fifty thousand pounds or so borrowed from the bank.)

What we had achieved so far at The New Piggery was a large 120- by 40-foot Dutch barn type building, double-skinned and insulated along three of the four sides. The fourth, you will remember, consisted of a row of heavy and unwieldy metal gates, which effectively nullified any good the expensive insulation on the other sides might have done. These sides had a six-foot-high, solid concrete block wall, designed to withstand the shoving of both pigs and the cleaning-out tractor. It was planned to convert this building into large pens to hold fifty to one hundred fattening pigs, with a meal store and mill-and-mixer at one end. This building, which at least when it was new looked quite impressive, was to our own design, and was meant to be what is known as 'multi-purpose', which usually means that it is not quite suitable for any particular purpose. How true! Fortunately, by one of those bizarre EEC rules, which encourage growth even though this merely increases unmanageable surpluses, the unit qualified for grant aid. This was because we could satisfy the condition that we could supply from the farm a given percentage of our own pig feed. It was certainly an enormous help financially.

For a fattening unit our building was undeniably too high, and Paul and I have often puzzled since over our exact reasons for making it so high. We can only assume that we were attracted by the relatively low cost of adding a few extra feet in height when the building was first erected, and we probably thought that if necessary we could build a loft above the pens for the storage of straw and for added insulation. This would have been an excellent idea, but has proved way beyond our resources then or since. From the beginning we have had to suffer derisory comments about our building not only from our Meat and Livestock Commission costings guru, but from other assorted experts who have visited us to try to help us to improve our overall performance.

But as things turned out it was our farrowing side in different quarters which gave us most worry. I am fairly unrepentant about our fattening unit, which housed large groups of pigs on deep litter – preferably shavings, of which we had an intermittent free supply. Intermittent because my son managed to divert most of them to his beef unit if we were not on the end of the phone at the right time. The pens were fronted by self-feeders, and fitted with water-bowls. From this unit at least our gradings were good, and our food conversions reasonable. But as with my own earlier prototype unit, metal parts over the years rusted to a paper thinness due to the noxious gases rising from the inmates. At The New Piggery we found that the steel stanchions and, particularly, those kamikazi metal doors, soon acquired a thick coating of rust, which the many sparrows who enjoyed a free indoor flying school dislodged and sent down the neck of any unwary visitor. We did enjoy a temporary respite from constant harassment by these feathered pests when one glorious day a kestrel got into The New Piggery and could not get out. One swoop of this graceful, fan-tailed bird down the length of the building cleared the twittering sparrows as if by magic. Sadly, all Paul's efforts at kestrel-training failed to keep this welcome predator confined for long.

At the time of the Great Move we had completed only three pens in this building. These were to be temporary accommodation for both the pigs from The Piggery and a load of store pigs from Suffolk partner Derek. We were anxious to get some sort of turnover going as quickly as possible, and the Suffolk pigs had been organised as a stop-gap replacement for those from one of our ex-regular suppliers. He had sensibly decided that expansion of his farm shop was not only a more profitable but a less frenetic enterprise than breeding pigs, and had dramatically ceased production overnight just when we needed it most. The demise of this efficient producer did not augur well for our own ambitious plans to become successful pig breeders.

Towards The New Piggery, standing isolated amidst Russell's partially-completed concrete apron and a natural sea of mud, sped the two cattle floats, with me perched in the leading cab and enjoying the ride hugely. The drivers, having got the bit between their teeth by forcing the hapless crane driver to give way, were in no mood to let any other mere road user stand in their path. What is more, as my driver reminded me at least every pulsating mile, they were already late for their next job. We cantered along narrow country lanes, overhanging branches scythed off and left flapping in the road by our back-draught, galloped through the environs of our local town, got a second wind on the relief road, swept round Tattenham Corner into the lane to our rural backwater, and achieved a sprint finish up the hill from The Bushes into the farmyard.

Panting, flanks heaving, steam rising through the side-vents from the violently jolted pigs, the two lorries crossed the finishing line and slithered to a halt. It was now that I really appreciated our wisdom in widening the entrance to The New Piggery. With brake lights and reversing lights flashing, gears grinding, the lorries backed with a shower of gravel from the spinning wheels through the double gates, missing the uprights by a whisker. They then headed (or rather, reversed) along the front of the three chicken houses served by the same entrance and onto the strip of new concrete leading to The New Piggery.

Well, one did. The other did not. My driver, with me to explain the geographical layout and to guide him back, managed the manoeuvre quite successfully, interpreting my 'left hand down', 'hard on that lock', 'right hand a bit', '*whoa*', more or less as meant. The other driver, trying too hard to give the guttering of the last chicken shed a wide berth, got

91

rather too close to the edge of the not-quite-set concrete. The edge of this slowly collapsed beneath the weight of his rear wheel, and the lorry lurched drunkenly into a nasty wet place inadequately filled with hardcore. The pigs all squealed with terror and rushed to the side of the lorry, which sank even further; the driver descended from his cab and swore mightily, displaying a surprising range of expletives for one normally so restrained.

With a great effort of will I stopped myself from sprinting round the corner of the building and into the safe haven of the neighbouring wood. Instead, I walked slowly round the back of the lorry, keeping well clear in case it decided to tip over on top of me, gave the driver a pitying look, and offered the age-old remedy, 'Let's all go and have a cup of tea.'

We now had one cattle float positioned to unload its pigs, and the other temporarily hors de combat, and threatening to block the exit of its mate. Having counted to one hundred and then having made a bold effort to view the scene dispassionately, I and the two drivers reached a compromise solution. My offer of a healing cup of tea was accepted. While we drank the tanniferous nerve-restoring brew we rang the haulage firm and warned them of the delay. Then we unloaded one lorry. Released from their respective compartments in the lorry, the sows were reunited with their litters, which they regarded with a mix of maternal ecstasy or complete indifference. They were then all herded off the lorry, through the first of our steel doors to be used constructively, and into a pen well provided with straw. There they settled to a life approaching normality once more, after a traumatic few hours. The driver of this lorry departed to his next job by squeezing successfully past the second lorry,

leaving us to cope with the task of extricating it. The pigs on this lorry had lapsed into an uneasy silence, broken only by the occasional squeal, as one shifted position and trod on another. They obviously feared the worst.

At this moment help arrived over the horizon. The convoy, headed by a proud Paul, came thundering up our lane, rather like a mechanised Captain Custard galloping to the relief of Mafeking (or wherever it was). Unfortunately, it met the cattle float going down. This time sheer weight of numbers forced the driver to give way, and a time-consuming reversal up a narrow lane back to the farm did nothing to help either his prompt arrival at his next job or his temper.

Paul's convoy had not travelled the ten miles or so between the two piggeries without incident. For one thing, the mill-and-mixer swayed and jerked most disconcertingly on the uneven platform of Des's lorry, threatening, or so Brian claimed (and he was driving right behind it) at any moment to snap the retaining ropes and crush his tiny sports car. Furious flashing of lights and sounding of horns at last persuaded Des to pull into a lay-by (he thought for a long time that all the signals he could dimly see in his cracked mirror were just the high spirits of youth), where he tightened the ropes and adjusted the blocks. Des was completely unperturbed by all the excitement.

'Quite safe, boyo,' he said with confidence, giving the mill-and-mixer an affectionate slap which moved it slightly.

As the convoy, like a circus on the move, or more accurately, a gang of diddicoys migrating from one filthy roadside verge to pollute another, drove along the dual-carriageway relief road of our local town, it was passed by a police patrol car. 'Just our blooming luck,' thought Paul, as with heart-stopping deliberation the gaudy vehicle slowed and pulled in front of him. However, its two occupants appeared engrossed in their conversation, and continued on their way, with no more than an amused sideways glance at the white, strained face of Alan, hunched over the wheel of our ancient Fordson, every bump in the road reverberating like a death knell in his throbbing head, every grunt of the tractor supplying his queasy stomach with noxious fumes.

The convoy had lost a number of its original members, as they peeled off in various directions to work, college or social security office, but it had picked up Russell and the only one of his concreting gang who had stayed the course, and who had belatedly surfaced from their warm couches. So there appeared at The New Piggery a motley crew of helpers. They all regarded the stricken cattle truck with amused concern, and as you can imagine, I received a fair bit of stick (the phrase 'almighty cock-up' sticks in the memory). My long-suffering wife was despatched to brew yet more tea while we reviewed the situation once again.

With the aid of the crane, which had followed to help unload the mill-and-mixer, and my most powerful tractor, we got the lorry back onto the hard concrete with surprisingly little trouble, knowing our par for the course, though there was one dreadful moment when the tow-rope suddenly slackened and the float threatened to keel over sideways.

With much relief the store pigs tumbled out of the lorry and into their new quarters, furnished with straw, short lengths of plastic pipe and several old tyres, to give them something to play with apart from each other. At least all the shouting, the lurching and the general confusion had helped to mix the different groups of pigs, and they settled down with only an occasional sign of aggression. Next door to them the sows were busy trying to identify their own litters, while the piglets showed much more interest in the sows with the best milk bar.

Paul was soon to find that the hurdling boar at The Piggery had obviously schooled his wives in his jumping technique before he met his premature end. Those gilts who had done their best to make him a battered boar might have rejected his person, but had practised his leaping skills assiduously. One or two of these when moved to The New Piggery showed promise for the Porcine Champion Hurdle or the Pig of the Year Show. Not only did they manage to leap the solid feeders fronting their own pen, but they then turned sharp left, and even without Harvey Smith to urge them on in his inimitable style, they cleared the feeders into the next pen. Paul would arrive to find two or three of the great brutes ensconced among the store pigs who, not unnaturally, viewed their invasion with some alarm. Meanwhile, the sow's own abandoned piglets were doing their vociferous best to bring the house down. On one occasion, a particularly athletic sow somehow managed to clamber over the four-foot dividing wall before Paul's very eyes. (More of her later.)

With all pigs unloaded, it was now the turn of the mill-and-mixer. Our grumpy crane driver had by now almost entered into the swing of things, and was proving quite co-operative. He had confided that it was his something ulcers, and he had been compelled to give up his 'only pleasure', smoking. He even raised a smile at the sight of Alan coughing his lungs out. He whipped the mill-and-mixer off with professional ease, making us suspect his earlier performance, and transferred it to its new site through the second of our steel doors to be used constructively. Here it was soon connected up by the electrician, who had throughout been an amused spectator of the goings-on. As the grinder whirred into action, a new era had begun.

Chapter Ten

'It is a mistake to suppose that any fool will make a farmer.' (R. S. Surtees)

AS I HEARD the mill-and-mixer whirr into action, I considered I had done my bit. Many weeks of planning had culminated in what, for us, was a reasonably successful move. Pigs and machinery were now in their new and permanent home, as was their minder, Paul. He faced the uphill task of getting this new unit into full production, which would not be at all easy, as it was still in a state of some disarray. After several days of unusual involvement I could relax once again and retire quietly, to mind my own affairs and to keep out of the way as far as possible.

I left Paul to organise his crew towards beer and hamburger and chips in Alan's pub, and retreated to the farmhouse to a belated but very welcome meal. Having washed down the pork chops – another of Paul's casualties – with several glasses of Beaujolais which I felt I had earned, I was able to tackle in my office the several days of accumulated post in euphoric mood. Among the mass of circulars advertising everything from thermal underwear (a must for winter racing) to spring bulbs (ditto for the garden), lurked a letter from an old friend and sparring partner of mine, John Elliot, now a well-known name in the pig industry. Early in his career John worked for the even better-known national company, Wall's, to whom I sold my pigs. I read his letter with interest, then, in reminiscent mood, slumped in an easy chair to reflect on the 'good old days', when their heavy hog producers nationwide were annually lectured, wined and dined in sumptuous style by Wall's, then under the dynamic and innovative chairmanship of the noble Lord Trenchard.

He was succeeded by a number of incumbents, all dedicated to the modern concepts of 'restructuring', 'rationalising', and 'making viable'. The pursuit of these questionable aims culminated in the sudden shutting of Wall's southern factory and an equally sudden announcement to their producers that they were no longer required. This was accompanied by a promise to help us find alternative outlets and a free buffet lunch, which did nothing at all to deaden the sense of outrage. Something akin, I imagine, to the feelings of a long-term loyal employee informed that he is redundant.

Whatever their capabilities, and they were usually considerable, there can have been few friendlier and more helpful teams than that of Wall's in those early days, and few more brilliant ideas than that of the heavy hog, a genuine multi-purpose pig, to which I have remained a devotee. We were an enthusiastic band of converts who descended in our hundreds upon the Great Wen (Cobbett's immortal phrase) together with our wives, eager for shopping, a unique free stay in a luxury hotel, where it seemed churlish in our country bumpkin way to complain of the heat and the noise, and a mammoth nosh-up and cabaret in Grosvenor House. Anticipating all this glamour we producers cheerfully listened in the morning to the assembled top brass telling us just what we were doing wrong, and how we could improve our performance.

One of the more extraordinary details that sticks in my mind was that it was necessary for heavy hogs to average a sale price of twenty pounds! (They now fetch four times that figure.) Otherwise, we were marketing them at below or above the maximum economical weight – 265 pounds. We were exhorted for our own good to pursue all the maxims of efficient production so beloved by the analyst. At our lecture sessions we were blinded with science and bombarded with graphs, statistics, and pretty coloured tables, in the presentation of which John E. had a considerable hand.

What a really splendid occasion it all was! How I regret the arid and soulless business ethic which now makes such shindigs unacceptable to accountants, inspectors of taxes, and other drab arbiters of our working lives. We are now condemned to a perpetual battle to keep up with the Joneses – well, the Japanese and the Germans actually – which outlaws most of the fun from business, and has not, in the view of this jaundiced writer, improved our lives one iota.

Few of us now have time to stand and jaw and have cups of coffee with the diminishing number of reps, advisers and other visitors who used to leaven the chore of cleaning out pigs with a shovel and wheelbarrow. Now the slurry sloshes into pits (or should do), is mechanically spread, and upsets the neighbours. Sows produce twenty-four and that surprising point-two piglets per year, who grow at an astonishing rate, eat less and less grub, and are (sometimes too) lean and meaty in the plastic wraps of the supermarket. We sit in our offices with our hardware, feeding its mechanical brain with data which only lets us know sooner rather than later that we are not doing very well.

Well, some of us do. Others bumble along as we always have done, being too old, or too stupid, or too stubborn, to try and change. At this point in my reverie I was forced, albeit reluctantly, to take issue with my old chum. In his letter he described me — among other things, which I will not repeat — as a pig farmer of 'questionable ability'. Now, there was no question about it at all. As readers of this saga will by now be only too aware, I am a pig farmer of very little ability. I always have been, and I always will be. How I have managed to scrape a living from the wretched brutes all these years is a mystery to all, particularly to my go-ahead son, who regards pigs as smelly, greedy and occupying room which should be filled by his cattle.

Unfortunately for him, poor old Paul allied himself to this paragon of incompetence at a time when pig-keeping was becoming an even more than usually hazardous occupation. I hasten to add that I would never have tempted him to join with me if I had been able to look into a crystal ball not clouded by optimism and false projections. In spite of his undoubted abilities — for instance, he understood computers — his hard work, and my encouragement, it was an uphill struggle from the beginning. Over the years we did a lot of things which at the time seemed reasonable, but afterwards proved distinctly dodgy.

One of these decisions was to borrow a lot of money from the bank to build our own unit. We struck a very bad time to do this, and we were in hock to the bank ever after, with very little prospect of ever reducing that great burden of debt. To make matters worse, this debt increased as we expanded slowly and painfully to our target of a hundred-sow unit. This was the sort of figure our cash-flow projections — produced by Paul on the back of the clipboard he used to record piglet mortality – told us we would need to obtain the necessary turnover to cover overheads and provide a living, let alone a profit.

The next missive I unearthed was much less pleasant. It was a telephone message taken down by my wife to inform me that the dreaded VAT person was to pay me a visit of inspection the following week, the first for many years. This news sent my pulses racing and my nerves on edge, for I was sure that over those many forgotten years I must have committed – quite unwittingly, I hasten to add – the most awful errors of omission and false accounting, all of which would be revealed by the searchlike scrutiny of the inspector. Would I be taken out and flogged, hung, drawn and quartered? Would it be appreciated that it was just human error, not deliberate chicanery? (But they all say that.) Would I be publicly humiliated in the local press?

I was not helped by my friendly accountant when I told him the news. He blithely informed me, 'They always find something. They have to.' When questioned by me on the competence or otherwise of my book-keeping, he said it was not too bad, 'about average I suppose. But then,' he added, 'that is not saying much.' Over the next few days with much labour and use of pocket calculator I brought my books up to date. And pretty vulnerable they looked.

Paul, who had recently survived an inspection without actually going to prison, was much more philosophical and less concerned than I was over these matters. But then, he was younger and understood modern maths. (My only hope was that my VAT person had heard Tom Lehrer sing, 'You don't have to get the right answer so long as you enjoy what you are doing.') I had a horror of dealing directly and in one's home with powerful officials (who can tear the place apart brick by brick if so minded), however pleasant they might be. Indeed, if they *were* pleasant, you became suspicious. I considered the whole thing a basic infringement of personal liberty. But that, I reflected, was a bee in my bonnet I must next week keep securely under lock and key. Which is where I feared I might end up.

However, my fears were groundless. When the dread day dawned I passed my VAT test with flying colours. A pleasant

99

young lady, accompanied by a trainee, went through the books of my two small farming companies with the Civil Service equivalent of a fine-toothed comb in one morning. 'Have you *really* finished?' I asked with amazement. I was actually complimented upon the way I kept my books. They were 'easy to understand' – a remark that I passed on to my accountant as quickly as possible, with a hint that in that case he should reduce his fees. He laughed.

None of the peccadilloes I feared I had committed were commented upon. Two matters were queried. Did our Daihatsu truck have seats and/or windows in the back? (No and No.) I took the inspector out to see the vehicle in the yard, and assured her we would never have bought it if the VAT was not reclaimable, which she was not certain about. She said she would check. We heard nothing further. In fact, we *had* bought seats for this vehicle, and had actually fitted one of them. Then we had been warned that if seats were fitted in the back it might make the whole vehicle VATable, so we whipped it out a bit quick. Unfortunately, the garage would not take them back. Nor was the lady inspector sure that a building I had sold from one company to another should have been VATed. I had carefully checked on this with my accountant, who said it should be, and I pointed out that as the VAT had both been paid and reclaimed – I hesitated to say I thought the whole operation a waste of time – it did not matter either way. That is to say, as both companies were registered and could reclaim VAT, it was really immaterial whether VAT should have been charged initially or not. 'Oh no,' she said, 'we must have it right.' Who was I to argue with such logic?

I must say I heaved a great sigh of relief to be given the VAT equivalent of a clean bill of health. Especially when I returned to my office, of which I had given the inspector the run, to find that I had forgotten to remove from my desk various indications (like my annual Newmarket badge) of a lifestyle not quite consistent with the image I had tried hard to portray of a hard-working, under-pressure farmer. I had debated with myself whether to appear from the yard, having ostensibly forgotten all about the visit, in my smelly overalls, but had rejected that as being all too obvious a ploy.

Over lunch we agreed that most VAT errors were mistakes

rather than deliberate, and that the real villains were unlikely to be caught because they were too clever and too bold. I have always considered this a general maxim. It is the silly idiot who keeps back a bit of cash and then puts it in a building society who cops it. The one who fiddles thousands, does not care or worry, and who spends the money on the Costa del Sol, gets away with it. Just one more example of how unfair life is!

A few weeks later I was able to sympathise deeply with a business friend of mine who after a similar inspection of his large company was presented with a VAT bill for some thousands of pounds. This was because an accounting method used for years and accepted by previous inspectors was not to the liking of the latest VATman, who declared imperiously, 'It's not good enough for *me*.' Nothing much my poor chum could do, except bite his lips ('only a young . . . too') and give his office staff an inordinate amount of extra work to supply the required information.

Chapter Eleven

'I'm not prepared to reveal the inner secrets of the water board to a member of the general public.' (J. Orton)

HOWEVER, THE hundred-sow unit referred to in the last chapter was just a pipe-dream as we unloaded our first pigs into The New Piggery. But at least we were in operation. Paul would no longer have to commute backwards and forwards twice daily between the two units, though he had many more visits to make to complete the necessary cleaning out and repairs to satisfy ourselves and our landlords that we had honoured our agreement. Russell had promised to complete the concreting before he returned to the unfrozen wastes of Canada. The electrician, the plasterer and the bricklayer were finishing the internal fitting-up, at times hindered by itinerant sows and a sexy boar. Envious as we were of the earnings of these craftsmen for a short working day compared with our rewards for tending livestock seven days a week, we were full of optimism and get-up-and-go.

Nonetheless, there were major problems confronting Paul at The New Piggery now that we had at long last completed our move. For one thing, apart from a large amount of often costly experience, and one profitable and one not so profitable year, we had not really progressed very far in our joint enterprise. Like Alice, we were almost back to square one again.

More serious, in spite of our determination not to move any pigs from one set of premises to another, because of the virulent outbreaks of swine dysentery and other well-known, not so well-known, and previously unknown diseases at The Piggery, this, like most good resolutions, was just made to be broken. In the end we had little option but to transfer our existing stock; mainly because the timing of the move went badly awry and many of the pigs were not big enough to sell, but also, as mentioned, because our principal weaner supplier had gone out of business. This meant we did not have an assured supply of good-quality pigs from one source (vital to contain disease) to put into the new building. At one foolishly optimistic moment we dithered with the idea of taking over his premises as well, and even went so far as to inspect them. Thank the Lord we did not!

So, in spite of all precautions and pious hopes, we managed to transmit a disease problem across ten miles of rural Hertfordshire. Not content with this, we exacerbated our difficulties by introducing rhinitis from pigs from my Suffolk partners, from whom we bought several loads to get us going and to bolster throughput. Derek and Gordon had been battling with this disease for years at great expense and trouble. In spite of an annual vet's bill of over five thousand pounds they were merely managing to contain rhinitis to a state where they could just about live with it. Finally, that problem at least was solved in dramatic fashion by confirmation of Aujeszky's disease on their unit, and by the wholesale slaughter of all their stock. The sense of desolation and despair felt by them, and the unnatural quiet following the slaughter of over three hundred sows and two thousand young stock, made our evacuation of The Piggery a relatively placid affair.

But at The New Piggery, the sight of a number of our fattening pigs looking (and behaving) like battered and punch-drunk prize-fighters, though odd and amusing to a layman, did nothing at all to improve our profitability there in the early days. Rhinitis also spread into our breeding herd when we eventually got that going, though fortunately never in a par-ticularly acute form. Only the occasional squashed snout and bloody snuffle and sneeze reminded us of our ill-luck, or our poor stockmanship; or both.

Paul also had to cope with the peculiar difficulties of a completely new building, not particularly well-designed for the job, with still sweaty concrete and plaster, and a lot of work still to be done to satisfy the personal idiosyncrasies of the piggy inhabitants. Not to mention their health status. For any new site takes a long time to settle down to the right mixture of bugs, etc., to give the inmates a relatively immune existence. All sorts of mysterious ailments are cheerfully explained by the vet as 'teething problems', which, he says, will all disappear as soon as the building becomes 'properly conditioned', whatever that may mean. Rather as 'whey bloat' covered any number of fatalities at The Piggery, so 'teething problems' covered a multitude of sins at The New Piggery, from deviant behaviour to outright villainy and murderous or suicidal intent.

The Chinese, in their wise way, rarely contemplate building anything of importance until the practitioners of Feng Shui have made sure that it will not lie 'in the path of the dragon'. There were times when we felt that we must have erected The New Piggery right on top of his tail. And we could certainly have used the services of the oracles of the I Ching, who foretell the future by scattering the pungent-smelling yarrow around the site. Though I doubt if even they would have quelled our initial enthusiasm.

But there were many compensations. It was a pleasant change for Paul to be able to walk out of his back door and across the road to work, and he was able to keep an eye on both The New Piggery and the chicken unit, which he was also running, through his kitchen window. This meant that the periodic emergency had less chance of developing into a major disaster.

Moreover, Paul's domestic existence was soon to take a turn for the more comfortable. For, through that well-known matrimonial agency, the local rugby club (not quite as successful as the Young Farmers' Club, but still pretty good), he was to acquire a New Wife to go with The New Piggery. This young lady's influence quickly produced order out of bachelor chaos in the bungalow. When I popped in for a cup of coffee the sink was no longer full of crockery, or the kitchen table littered with beer bottles, the Sunday papers, the remains of breakfast and correspondence, including that latest discouraging report from our MLC guru. Even better, this young lady had that essential attribute to a Good Wife, a Job of Her Own (well paid). Her income did much to smooth the stony financial path over the next year or so.

Now that we had at last moved in, our primary objective at The New Piggery was once again to establish and to expand a fattening pig enterprise, then to diversify slowly and carefully into breeding. If you recall, we had already given this a trial run and had learned at least that Paul enjoyed working with sows and had a rapport with their unpredictable behaviour. This essential facility is too often ignored by those of our advisers who know little of the practicalities of farming. It is no good milking cows if you hate the clumsy brutes and getting up early in the morning, even though your farm may be suited to little else. Sell up and go into life insurance. It had also painfully taught us that learning from books and as you go along is no real substitute for practical experience with an expert. For this day and age Paul was amazingly literate, but short on experience.

The few sows we had brought over with us from The Piggery were disposed of as soon as their piglets were weaned. Or, more accurately, when those piglets were abandoned when their mums jumped into the next pen, snuggled down with the alarmed fatteners, and refused to go back. They obviously considered a good old nosh-up on fattening grub and a quiet siesta preferable to continually being punched and trodden on by their greedy progeny, squabbling for the diminishing supply of mother's milk. With some relief we watched these sows, active as ever, hurdle their way up the ramp of the lorry. They had been beginning to be more than just an embarrassment, with their penchant for demolishing whatever we had just erected, particularly any stack of newly arrived feedstuffs.

The driver told us later, with great glee, that the most athletic of this group astonished the unloading slaughterman by taking a flier from the back of the lorry, and, having got a good run, clearing with one mighty leap two of her mates who were dithering on the ramp. Fortunately she landed in the greasy passage of the abattoir and slithered on her rump towards her maker. The mind boggles at the thought of where she might have jumped had she realised what lay in store for her. But, in spite of what the 'animal-lovers' lobby may say, in my experience – which is what most of our critics lack – animals are not unduly worried by blood and guts. When I used to deliver pigs to a small abattoir right next to a railway station in the middle of a town I noticed that if the holding pen was full they wandered quite happily through the slaughterhouse itself to the killing pen. Needless to say, the local authority shut this long-established business down, following representations from today's more susceptible folk, who objected to a slice of life, or death, on their doorstep.

We soon realised that the sort of fattening enterprise we were able to run at The New Piggery, particularly as we were anxious not to take pigs from more than one source, which would be unlikely to provide an adequate supply, was not going to produce sufficient turnover to justify our heavy overheads. So we had to push on more quickly than we had intended with our plans for a breeding herd. Because of our disease problems in the past, and now unfortunately in the present, we were also anxious to establish a closed herd, introducing high-performance boars as and when we could afford them.

Strange to relate, we did over the next few years purchase a number of top-quality boars and gilts from the pig-breeding company which, to our great surprise, temporarily took over The Piggery some time after we finally shook its slurry from our wellies. Paul got to know the very capable young manager through the YFC. If he had surplus stock, or cancelled orders, he offered them to us at a bargain price. Being, quite rightly, very health conscious, he shied away from any contact with such dangerous beings as Paul and me, unloading his charges at the gates to the chicken unit, and beating a hasty retreat when Paul approached to drive these elite creatures, treading deli-cately on their expensive trotters, to their new and less hygienic quarters.

The first priority for our new breeding unit was obviously to build accommodation for sows. In this connection it is interest-ing how life goes full circle. For when I bought my present farm in 1959 – farmhouse, cottage, bungalow, some buildings (for cows), 90 acres of land, £9250, extra 50 acres of land available for £2250, Oh, Dear! – the first building I erected was an 'Arcon' prefab.

To digress for the benefit of my younger readers, these prefabs were erected just after the last war as 'temporary' accommodation for those returning from the forces or those made homeless by bombing. They were sectional asbestos, steel-framed bungalows, well insulated, and quickly put up on prepared sites. Like many other equally splendid ideas, they were the product of a national crisis. They were intended to last ten years, by when it was estimated the housing stock would be replenished by traditional buildings. Pious hope! Forty years on the group built in my village, some half-mile from the centre as they were reckoned to be ugly and vulgar, were still occupied. With increasing affluence the tenants could at least drive in their cars rather than walk the steep hill to the local shop which is the last survivor of four. The bus which used to pass their door hourly now does so just once a day.

So, while scores of high-rise flats, acres of town redevelopment, have come and gone, fallen down or been blown up, the humble prefab, where unmolested, goes on serenely providing acceptable and cheap accommodation. Many thousands of them, taken down, transported and re-erected, have enjoyed a second lease of life as farm buildings of one sort or another. Mine is a workshop, those of my Suffolk partners are adapted for farrowing sows, and have recently been internally sprayed with foam to improve insulation. There is no reason, so far as I can tell, why, with proper maintenance, they should not go on for ever. Indeed, since writing the above, I have been to a car race meeting at Snetterton, where several of these prefabs have recently enjoyed a facelift, and as canteens, workshops and offices, look almost as good as new. I imagine they were originally built on the airfield during the war over forty years ago.

It was thus natural that when we came to consider possible buildings for our sows at The New Piggery, I should suggest these prefabs as a cheap and practical possibility. Scanning the advertisement columns we found a firm still supplying them at about eight times the price I had paid for mine a quarter of a century ago. Another sign of the times was that when the building eventually arrived the suppliers told us that they had had to cannibalise several in order to obtain one complete and undamaged, due to vandalism on the site the moment the tenants moved out. Even then, most of the glass in the windows was broken.

Although it is perfectly possible to erect these buildings oneself, due to pressure of work and fears of incompetence, we thought it well worth paying the two hundred and fifty pounds asked by professional erectors to do the job. This gang were jovial East Enders (not the TV variety), who whipped up the building in a couple of days, managing to break the rest of the glass in the process and to astonish the locals in the pub with their coarse wit. Like most town-dwellers, they were amazed at

107

some of the things which go on in the country. Apart from considering us idiots to work in the conditions we do, it is always a culture shock to see your vacuum-packed Sunday pork joint running around and looking quite intelligent, and to learn, for instance, that pigs have to be bled before the meat is considered edible. They helped load pigs into our trailer with a new awareness, slapped them affectionately on the rump, and told them to make sure they had plenty of crackling.

It is surprising how quickly one becomes friends with characters who work hard and make jokes. We were quite sorry to see them get into their battered truck and drive back to the big city, where they openly admitted to 'ripping off' the more naive of their employers in a number of ingenious ways which I shall not disclose in case I ever need to use them myself.

We were left with the shell of a twenty- by thirty-foot building, with rather tatty roof insulation only, and without gutters (which had disappeared in the move), into which we were to fit farrowing crates, etc. These, and other essential second-hand fixtures and fittings, we located and bought under rather ironic circumstances. Paul answered an advertisement in the local paper, and went to view a mass of equipment from a redundant pig unit, much of which was suitable for us, but had to be bought *in situ*.

So Paul contacted his friend Des, who we last met helping us move from The Piggery, and who, with his knowledge of, and contacts in, the pig industry, had been a tower of strength to us. Des was a cheerful soul with a large beer paunch and strong as the proverbial ox. He and Paul spent many laborious away-days dismantling stalls, crates, and feeders, having to chip many of them out of hard concrete. They were then loaded on to Des's lorry and transported – if that is the correct word to describe the hiccuping progress of Des's ancient vehicle – through the byways of rural Herts (avoiding major roads for obvious reasons) to The New Piggery.

It was hard, sweaty and thirsty work. Fortunately there was a pub handy (there always does seem to be when folk like Des are around), and there Des and Paul used to retire for their lunch break. Paul recalls the first occasion when they went into the bar and ordered two pints, and two chicken and chips. After a brief while Des returned to the bar and asked for 'the same again'.

'Two more pints?' asked the landlord.

'No,' replied Des, 'Two more pints *and* two more chicken and chips.' From then on, the landlord would have two pints on the counter as he heard the lorry grate to a halt, and two double portions of chicken and chips in the deep fryer as Paul and Des exploded through the door.

It was only after a trip or two that the penny dropped and we realised that the pleasant man selling off the equipment was none other than the ex-managing director of a pig-buying group which had recently gone up the spout owing me some three thousand five hundred pounds and lots of others lots more. My poor old haulier, a hard-working genuine chap if ever there was one, was dropped in it to the tune of some seven thousand pounds. We eventually – well over a year later – got a few pence in the pound after the vultures had picked the bones clean. The ex-MD had apparently decided that pig-keeping was about as dodgy as running a group, and was busy turning his buildings over to a farm shop. It is an ill wind, etc.

I must admit to all sorts of ignoble thoughts about paying for the equipment we purchased, but morality prevailed, and we not only acquired but also paid for a mass of miscellaneous stuff, much of which – and I must admit the ex-MD was generous in his dealings – we took on the adage that it 'will come in useful one day'. (It is still in a heap.) Farrowing crates and sow feeders are not the easiest of articles to transport safely, and Des's lorry appeared never to have recovered completely from the trauma of moving the mill-and-mixer. The sides bulged at the best of times, and on the penultimate journey when a crate slipped from the top of the load and landed hard against one side it gave way altogether, allowing the crate to continue its headlong fall. Fortunately, a metal leg jammed in the gap between the side and the floor of the lorry, and stopped it falling completely off into the road. However, enough of it hung over the side to send a shower of sparks into the path of following motorists, and to put the fear of God into Paul.

It is surprising what strength one possesses when driven by panic, and Paul and Des were out of the cab, the errant crate disentangled, thrown back on top of the others, roped in, and the journey resumed almost as quickly as it takes to write this down. Even the carefree Des was seen to glance anxiously now and again into his cracked mirror, and he and Paul turned into the farm lane with a huge sigh of relief. Having arrived safely at The New Piggery, the two musketeers transferred with more sweat and tears – especially when Paul inadvertently dropped his seven-pound sledge-hammer on Des's foot – such of the load as was usable into the first of our prefabs. This was to be the home of the nucleus of the herd which was going to make our fortune.

After the first few months at The New Piggery a certain amount of order was beginning to arise out of chaos. The concreting had been completed, and Russell had returned to Canada with the current acolyte, there to continue his ambitious task of building what looked from the photographs to be a cross between an Elizabethan manor house and a log cabin. As he laboured away, hauling logs, splitting timbers, and constructing his dream home to his own design, he camped out on the other side of the clearing, joined for short spells by friends and relations who lent him a hand. Many of these also possessed Russell's determination to create an idyllic community; the eternal hope of visionaries throughout time. Quiet and committed, Russell shook the mud of The New Piggery off his wellies, and jetted off to his private plot in the Canadian backwoods, grateful I am sure to be released from even a tenuous connection with the production of meat for human consumption. Not to mention the strains of driving on his wayward concreting gang to complete the job, and to stay away temporarily from the social security office and/or the pub.

110

The internal divisions in The New Piggery had also been completed and plastered. The plasterer had slapped on sand and cement with that enviable skill which looks so easy, but when imitated results in more plaster on the floor than on the wall. Even that which does stick at first, peels off as it dries. In the process he earned a fortune which we could ill afford, but we felt it essential to have walls which could be easily washed. Paul had fitted water-bowls in each pen. True to form the supply pipes to these bowls were initially draped elegantly along the building, to be tidied up one day, but meantime a tempting target for any inexperienced driver of the tractor and front bucket when cleaning out the pens. As a result, this job was occasionally interrupted by a great fountain of water from a pipe wrenched from a joint. Paul would repair the break, philosophically remarking that it made the pressure hosing of the pen that much easier.

The pens were filled by a motley collection of pigs, partly from my Suffolk partners, and partly from other suppliers, whom we had to accept in order to achieve a reasonable throughput. This was completely against our initial determination only to have pigs from one source, in order to minimise disease risk, but had been forced on us by the loss of our principal supplier. The problems associated with taking pigs from different sources into a new building, into which we had already imported many of our disease traumas, increased our resolve to push ahead with the establishment of our own breeding herd, which would hopefully eventually supply all the pigs we wished to fatten.

About the only thing we got right in those early days was to continue the friendly and helpful arrangement with our pig buyer, who said encouraging things about the end result of all our endeavours when it hung in the abattoir. As he was also less fastidious than some about casualties, and was within easy reach, he was a valuable outlet for all those odds and sods of pigs, the lame, the halt, and the no-doers, which only we seemed to produce. Unfortunately, he shut at the weekend, when most of our emergencies seemed to occur. Do pigs *know* it is Sunday, and that they will get a shot of penicillin rather than the chop if they act ill?

Paul was fully occupied looking after the chicken unit as well as coping with the pigs, not to mention his expeditions with Des and our attempts to expand. Somehow he still managed to enjoy the odd game of rugby, though he did draw the line at far-away games. As he said, 'It's not so much having to leave almost immediately after the game which bothers me. It's trying to prise the drunken bums who came with me out of the bar which is so difficult.' And when he did get back it was often to discover that, freed from supervision for a few hours, the inmates had managed to create havoc in one part or another of his piggy penitentiary. I do not think that they ever actually climbed on the roof and hurled slates at him as he drove up, but I certainly would not have it put it past them.

After a great deal of hard work, Paul and Des had rescued enough equipment from the redundant piggery of the ex-MD to set us up as pig breeders. That is, once much of it had received remedial treatment, and the necessary fixtures and fittings had been installed in the shell of the prefab. And here we met a small snag. The farrowing crates which Paul and Des had so laboriously chipped from their concrete pads were too large to go through the doors. These, of course, were only house-doors, through which generations of Brummies had passed in and out in the course of their several lives. (The prefab had come from a site in inner Birmingham.) This quandary led to a great deal of head-scratching, and provoked a number of interesting suggestions, some of which, considering the educational attainments of the parties – for this was a weekend and Paul had mustered his friends – were frankly surprising. 'Why don't you stuff it down the chimney?' said one wag, and received a look which would have stopped a lesser man in his tracks.

In the end it was unanimously decided by a majority of one (Paul) that we would have to take out the large window which had originally lit the sitting-room of the prefab, giving a pan-oramic view over the Birmingham building site, where high-rise flats were being erected to replace these decent detached homes with small gardens. To remove the window was nothing like as simple as it appeared, for the window was metal and had been re-screwed with new long screws into the wooden frame, an integral part of the building. However, time and Paul and his mates wait for no one, and the window was soon successfully eased from its frame after a short skirmish, which threatened at one time to cause a major collapse of the front of the prefab, rather like that in the Laurel and Hardy movie.

Once the window had been removed it was a relatively simple job to manhandle the farrowing crates through the opening, though in the process at one stage Brian nearly lost his doctorate. With a hockey-field jink and a backward leap onto Alan's toes he just managed to avoid the descending leg of a sliding crate.

'Gosh, that was a near thing,' he exclaimed, turning an even whiter shade of white than usual. (He had just got engaged.) By juggling around we succeeded in fitting in eight crates, with a narrow passage fore and aft for feeding one end of the sow and clearing away the surplus from the other end.

As time passed and we learned of the disadvantages of the prefab the hard way, we made various modifications. We made efforts to improve the ventilation; we constructed new creeps for the piglets, who would insist on snuggling up to their mum just as the old fool turned over and lay down on them; we put in extra rails to try and prevent this over-lying; and we erected an internal division to split the building into two parts, so each half could be washed and rested at a time. None of these amateurish efforts did much to stop a much-too-high piglet mortality rate (up to 18 per cent at times), just one of the many reasons why we consistently failed to make a decent profit. There is nothing more frustrating than to have pigs born, only to lose them just when they should be getting out of trouble. Whenever I saw a look of dejection on Paul's face I guessed the maternity unit was playing up again.

Our first prefab was joined fairly quickly by another, this to provide accommodation for sows in stalls, where they were tethered. This was the system we acquired from the ex-MD, and in spite of initial qualms we were fairly happy with it. It has the great advantage that a large number of sows can be housed economically, fed individually, and observed closely as they approach farrowing. This second prefab was erected by Russell when he returned from Canada the next winter, using the first one as a model. They are quite tricky things to erect, unless you know where each individual section should go, and those parts made of steel and containing a door and a window were particularly awkward and heavy. Especially if, as rarely happened, they still had glass in them. Russell proudly showed us photos of the progress of his Canadian house, which made any of our structural problems fade into insignificance.

The original siting of the first prefab for the sow unit had posed quite a problem. Wherever we were to put it, we realised we were going to be faced with yet more concreting, for The New Piggery and its concrete yard adjoined the chicken unit along one side. So any expansion had to be behind and on the other side of the building, on fresh ground. As we had had quite enough concreting to last us several lifetimes already, we put the prefab as close to The New Piggery as we could, leaving only a small gap between the two buildings. When Russell had erected the second prefab alongside the first, this gap proved a useful alleyway to drive sows along from their stalls or their farrowing crates to new quarters. These were either a rickety wood/string/asbestos/corrugated-iron dry-sow yard, or one of the pens in The New Piggery, still having to be used for sows.

Unfortunately this convenient gap was economy-sized, and the better upholstered of our matrons found it difficult, if not impossible to negotiate. They would get stuck half-way, would start that high-pitched screaming which travels straight through the human brain taking much of the intervening grey matter out with it, and they would refuse even to try to move either way. Any companions would be jammed up behind their panicky colleague. They would try to turn round, which was impossible, then the more agile would back up a pace or two until meeting some unseen or imagined obstacle, which would propel them forward again. The stuck sow would receive the full force of their forward rush, and would get jammed even tighter. Over in the farmhouse my soporific study of the form from Newmarket would be disturbed by the sound of mayhem, the bristles on the dog would rise in alarm, and the pigs in my own unit would begin to join in the chorus.

'Hullo, what's going on up there?' my neighbour would ask his brother as they worked away with bagging hook and scythe on the hedge of a field a mile away. 'The Lord only knows,' would be the reply. Both of these delightful olde-world characters regarded the goings-on at The New Piggery with considerable scepticism and wonder, having been born and reared in an age when half-a-dozen sows was a large enterprise.

114

As quickly as it had started, the noise would suddenly stop. Having witnessed it, I knew what had happened. Paul had clambered over the top of the rearmost sow, small board in hand, and with that to her face had backed her out of the runway. He would repeat this as often as necessary until he reached the cause of the hold up. This poor brute would prove more difficult to shift, but on the principle that what goes in must come out, she would eventually be persuaded to give one final backward heave, and would release her buttocks from whatever had first detained them – usually a slightly protruding sheet of asbestos at the back of the prefab.

This was only the first stage of the rescue. The released sows had by now either got out into the yard and made a break for freedom, or had got back into their respective prefabs, where one or two snuggled down quite happily with a bag of meal as a pillow, and the others started a frantic search for the piglets which had just been weaned from them. Whichever, Paul would have a difficult time rounding them up, and then persuading them to retrace their steps up the alleyway between the buildings, which, not unnaturally, they regarded with a great deal of suspicion by now. Somehow he would manage it, usually just as I arrived on the scene, having torn myself away from the beguiling voice of John Oaksey or 'Broughie'.

I never ceased to be amazed at how much Paul could accomplish all on his own. He would sort out pigs from a pen of fifty, weigh them, load them or move them over unfenced areas without any apparent undue difficulty. I rarely saw him flustered, though I saw him hot and sweaty many times, but he would still raise a wry smile as I came round the corner. I think he thought it a reflection upon his ability if he had to ask for help. Besides which, the sort of help I offered was so critical, and so easily degenerated into bad temper and violence to dumb critturs, that he probably rightly considered he was better off without it. Nor was it that he had a galaxy of ingenious non-human aids to help him. Paul was very much a make-do-and-mend sort of chap, and never seemed to worry that the door of his weighing machine would burst open at a critical time because the catch had rusted, or that the barriers he erected collapsed beneath the weight of live pigmeat. He just fetched the pigs back and started all over again. I do not know what a time and motion expert would have made of it all, but Paul got by.

As it turned out, Paul's amiable and unflurried disposition was vital to the retention of his sanity during the years of our joint enterprise, even if it did let him accept working conditions and practices which would have irked others. If I remonstrated with him his invariable reply was, 'I'll do it as soon as I have the time.' It was a classic Catch-22 situation, further aggravated by our continual shortage of money. It was not just almost essential repairs and improvements which got postponed, but smaller things as well. For instance, the scrurrying about of an army of rats when he paid his late-night visit to the unit never seemed to bother him unduly. Only the loud complaints of temporary helpers left in charge who were taken aback by the glinting of red eyes from the food troughs galvanised him to do something about it. He was pleasantly surprised when liberal dosings of rat-bait in strategic places reduced the problem, though not so pleased when he kept discovering dead bodies in unexpected places.

At one time we employed on my farm a young man who spent some of his pre-college year with us. As with most temporary help on the farm he was quickly shunted over to The New Piggery where there was most need of assistance. Indeed, one of the advantages of our move from The Piggery was the occasional availability of labour to help Paul out, though not everyone took kindly to the peculiar challenge presented by our unit. We christened this very pleasant young man, another William, by the sobriquet, 'Young Billaiki', which is an affectionate Greek corruption of 'William'. This was to differentiate him from my own son William, and the real, Senior Billaiki, who was a great family friend and had earned his nickname by years of fraught travail with Greek shipowners. Young Billaiki was given a few days to get used to it all, and then left in charge for a day. He was greatly taken aback by the number of sows who managed to release themselves from their tethers overnight and were wandering about in the sow stalls building when he went to feed them.

When this happened to Paul he quite cheerfully coaxed them back into their places and tightened the tethers. Which goes some way to meet the criticisms of the system. If sows hated tethers wild horses would not get them back in them a second time. But to achieve this painlessly you required the necessary experience that Young Billaiki lacked, and it would take him an age to replace the strays, while all the others waited impatiently with slobbering jaws for their delayed feed. His arrival at our breakfast table, late, red-faced, hot and flustered, and his announcement that he was 'completely shattered', became a regular occurrence during his stay. Mind you, his overnight indulgences at young farmers' clubs and similar establishments of a convivial nature, where he was a great favourite with the opposite sex, may have had something to do with the last statement. He and my William would shake their heads unsympathetically over the shortcomings of Paul's unit. 'You'd better come and help me relief milk tomorrow,' William would say. 'Not ruddy likely,' Young Billaiki would reply. He had enough trouble surfacing at 7.00 am. 'I'll stick to those old sows.'

To give Young Billaiki his due, he adopted Paul's independent spirit, and nearly always managed to right things on his own. Just occasionally, as when our randy boar attempted to force an entrance into a group of unresponsive sows, did he call for help. Paul always greeted the vivid descriptions of such calamities with mild amusement, and fetched yet another piece of baler-twine or erected yet another makeshift barrier. Pallets left behind on the farm were a favourite for the latter. But not with me. For the pigs would get their noses through the gaps and bang the pallets up and down with great pleasure.

With the two prefabs in use, Paul realised that however much straw and/or shavings he used, he was still going to have a drainage problem from them. We were far too near a footpath, which was used, it seemed to us, only by a continuous file of eagle-eyed conservationists, for us to pipe any effluent straight into the nearest ditch. This was, I blush to confess, my first suggestion. In the good old days nobody thought twice about such a manoeuvre. In fact, in the circles in which I moved, it was par for the course, most farmers being enthusiasts for the uncomplicated solution, and not that bothered about the scruples of outsiders. Nowadays, while acid rain kills our forests and nuclear power station explosions send out clouds of lethal radiation, the slightest suggestion that your pig effluent may be

117

polluting a watercourse miles away is enough to land you in court.

We had direct experience of such suspicions a year or so later. Following a very wet winter a seepage from our dung-heap formed a small puddle of slurry in the neighbouring wood. Well, it was a wood – a real wood – until modern forestry clean-felled all the deciduous timber and replanted with regimented, dark and menacing conifers. This environment-destroying puddle was spotted by two eagle-eyed and officious ramblers, who complained via the local council to the water board. This caused us no end of trouble. Letters passed backwards and forwards, and we received visits from an attractive river-lady. Fortunately, she was both understanding and recognised the problems faced by livestock farmers, especially in a prolonged wet spell. Yet she possessed Draconian powers if she deemed we were not obeying the stringent regulations. We could even have been shut down. Eventually I suggested a meeting on site between all interested parties to discuss the problem. Needless to say, those who had stirred up all the trouble in the first place had never seen fit to approach me direct. At the arranged time Paul, son William and I, the river-lady, and the public health inspector all turned up at The New Piggery. We drank coffee and waited. The complainants, plus the representative of the local authority, did not put in an appearance.

It was some satisfaction to me to be able to point out to the annoyed officials that the walkers had in any case been tres-passing in a private woodland, with whose owners we had always enjoyed most amicable relations, and from whom we had never received a vestige of a complaint. I was even more satisfied to receive a copy of a letter from the river-lady which she wrote to the complainants, emphasising the point I had made, and stating that neither she nor the public health inspector could find any cause for concern. Such costly inter-ferences seem nowadays to be a regular feature of the lives of those trying to make a living in the country. I am sure there is a moral there somewhere.

As so often since he had entered into our lives as a purveyor of sweet-smelling whey and general good tidings, Des came up with a suggested solution. It so happened, he said, that he knew where he could lay his hands on a large, strong, disused chemical tank which would solve the problem of effluent from the prefabs. 'You can sink it into the ground, and pipe the effluent into it. When it's full, just pump the stuff into your spreader or straight onto the manure heap.' (You can see why we had so much trouble later on.)

'So we need a pump as well,' said Paul.

'No problem,' said Des, 'I know someone with a suction pump he wants to get rid of. Leave it to me.'

Nothing daunted by our record of similar operations, usually made doubly difficult by our need to do everything on the cheap, we decided to install the tank, which Des volunteered, for a moderate sum and his 'vittels' (chicken and chips again) to supply and deliver. The lorry which had served us so loyally in the past was, apparently, still chundering on, geriatric but game. A neighbourhood contractor, after some persuasion, agreed to send over a machine from a local job to dig a hole and unload the tank into it, if we managed to spirit a pig (dead and cut up) into a hole in his deep freeze.

He was as good as his word. His machine arrived on time on site and in no time at all scooped out a mammoth hole. It then stood there pulsating gently, the driver smoking in his cab, awaiting the arrival of Des with the tank. Some two hours later the driver was smoking out of the top of his head. There was still no sign of Des. Then we had a phone call from a 'Happy Eater' on the A45. A voice which sounded as though it was speaking through a hamburger said, 'I've broken down boyo. But don't worry. My mate, who's a top class mechanic, is on his way. I'll be with you in no time at all.' He eventually arrived just as it was getting dark, the victim (he said) of a diesel blockage.

Meanwhile, the digger driver had announced in no uncertain terms that he was off back to his original job, where 'the foreman will be going spare'. Only bribery and corruption of the most blatant kind persuaded him to return the next morning. But this meant that we had to detain Des overnight which, given his capacity for the good life, was expensive, if hilarious. Early next morning he and Paul staggered from the bungalow, blinking blearily in the bright light, and looking as though they had slept in their clothes. (They had.) The tank crouched menacingly on the lorry, like some great fat slug. It looked as if it, too, had had a bad night. The digger came

lurching noisily up the narrow lane, swiping off branches of trees as it swayed from side to side. The large hole was full of water.

Using the expertise acquired from moving the whey tank and the mill-and-mixer unit, we swathed the tank in ropes and chains, hooked it to the digger arm, and it was unloaded quite easily into the hole. It must have weighed a couple of tonnes at least. It floated around like a toy duck, or, more accurately, a plastic submarine, in a child's bath-tub. Folding the notes into his back pocket the driver and his digger left us to it. We stood around the hole in a circle and scratched our heads. Des asked, 'Anyone got an alka-seltzer?'

Paul, his degree in chemical engineering coming to the fore, suggested we filled the tank with water. We did. It was surprising how much it held, and how long it took. Paul and Des fed the pigs and had breakfast. Revived, they returned to the scene of action. The tank still floated. With a borrowed pump we pumped out the water from the hole, trying to make a dry dock of it. The tank settled slowly and majestically and with a vulgar squelch upon the mud on the bottom, and we hastily shovelled in the soil around it. By the afternoon the tank was quite obviously floating again. We thrust it back into its grave by running our heaviest tractor on to it. We then poured concrete all around it. The job was becoming expensive.

For two days we dared not move the tractor. When we eventually did pluck up courage to do so – oh, so gingerly! – to our great relief it did appear that the tank had settled, although the outlet was off centre. We congratulated ourselves prematurely. By the next morning it had risen again some eighteen inches from the depths, and its curved metallic top was above ground. In that position it has remained since; though we sometimes feel that if we were ever to empty it entirely it would pop out of its concrete coffin like some gigantic champagne cork!

Otherwise, it served its purpose well though, like the slurry pits at The Piggery, it always needed emptying at the most inconvenient time. The gurgling and bubbling which took place when we opened the top was quite eerie, rather like the introductory shots to a horror movie. Surprisingly, no animal, human or otherwise, slipped into it. So far as we know.

Chapter Twelve

'If you are already up to your neck in water a ripple can drown you.' (Chinese proverb)

PAUL NEVER did approach the organised discipline of many well-run herds, where all the sows farrow when they should (even if they have to be induced), all the piglets are weaned on certain days, and AI works first time. This was partly due to inexperience but also, I am convinced, to the deliberate deception of some of the more awkward of our should-be pregnant matrons. These seemed to take a malicious pleasure in demanding at least two separate services from our Lothario of a boar (and given his virtuosity who can blame them?), thus postponing their planned farrowing date; or in pretending they were about to farrow, having to be moved to the farrowing crates, and then failing to produce for several days. Just for a variation the occasional sow would start farrowing down early in the sow stalls. This was a most inconvenient place, and it was a messy and tiresome business trying to transfer the errant sow to more suitable quarters.

As a result, we never had enough farrowing crates to make life easy, for us or the sows. We converted a corner of The New Piggery into an emergency maternity ward, but this was rather cold and draughty and required expensive insulation, and still did not give us enough places. Even with a large margin of error built into our statistical programme – so many sows, so many farrowings a year, so many weeks in the farrowing crates, etc. – I would often visit The New Piggery to find a sow and her brand new litter in temporary accommodation of straw bales at the end of the feeding passage. Fortunately, they often did as well under these conditions as in a more controlled environment.

Taking our courage in both hands, for it is always disconcerting to find out exactly how bad you are, we had started costing with the Meat and Livestock Commission (MLC). Paul really rather enjoyed figures, and his records, though untidily kept on a dirty clip board, which had a habit of disappearing between the stacks of concentrates in the meal-store, were quite comprehensive. These figures were transferred to the complicated returns demanded by the MLC, fed into their computer, and regurgitated on reams of perforated paper, which landed with an ominous flop in Paul's hallway. It was followed soon after by our particular MLC expert, a dynamic and attractive young lady, who lectured us severely on our shortcomings. Sadly, in spite of all her ministrations, reinforced by the advice of a specialist vet we later called in, we never did manage to approach the sort of performance figures which would have offered us some encouragement.

In all the seven years of our association, Paul rarely allowed himself a holiday of longer than a day or so, and he was, of course, on duty seven days a week, especially after we had set up our breeding herd. Difficult as it was for Paul and I to get away together, we now determined to visit the annual National Pig Fair. Leaving Young Billaiki in charge, we shot off up the MI in Paul's pick-up, which smelt strongly of the meal spilled in the flat back and sent putrid by days of rain.

Much as we enjoyed the day overall, it was nevertheless a humiliating experience. Hidden away in our neck of the woods we had carried on sublimely in our 'also-ran' way, with only the periodical unnerving interruption from guru, accountant or bank manager to stop us short in our tracks. On one occasion we had even been persuaded to produce a cash-flow analysis for our bank to justify the optimistic noises we always made. Like the figures in most of those documents, our projections turned out to be wildly awry, mainly because the price of pigs dropped unexpectedly by ten pence a kilo, which meant about five pounds a pig to us. Much more than our profit!

But at the Pig Fair every step and every stand produced evidence that not only were we inadequately equipped and our set-up amateurish in the extreme, but that our (piggy) performance was even worse than we suspected. Moreover, the car park was crammed with the expensive cars and four-wheel drives of the successful, besides which Paul's truck looked like a poor relation. Any similar vehicles were, somehow, quite obviously second strings, or, even more obviously, just kept for the shooting. Inside, the whole place was thronged with pig farmers exuding confidence and competence. The snatches of conversation which came our way did nothing to diminish our sense of isolation.

'I've increased to three hundred sows.'

'My new fattening house works a treat. Cut days to slaughter by five.'

'I don't get quite those sort of results. But then I don't believe *he* does either.'

'See you at the Royal.'

'Did you say two point *four* litters a year?'

A stroll through the demonstration unit really gave us the depressions. There, white-coated experts and information printed on plastic boards explained how the unit was producing more and more pigs at less and less cost from the specially designed, on-test buildings, which bore as much relationship to our Piggery as the QE II to a tramp steamer. Our 'own' young lady smiled and waved at us. She always gave the impression that she considered us just slightly mad. She talked earnestly to us until diverted by one of her 'top-third' clients, who was querying amino acid levels. I did not have the faintest idea what amino acid level was, but Paul knew.

Sows, supine in their technological farrowing crates, regarded their twelve healthy offspring with quiet pride, and ignored the stares of visitors. The predecessors of those twelve had shot through the all-in-one fattening house in record time to provide the modern housewife with the lean, not very tasty (because too young) meat she likes to see on the supermarket shelves and to cook in her microwave. Boars lay massive and obedient in their pens, well aware that any show of the sort of aggression or sexual exuberance so prevalent at The New Piggery would lead to their immediate succession by a test-tube. Paul and I told each other that, of course, we were only seeing the best; that they, too, must have the occasional litter of one; the occasional runt who always rushes to the front of the pen when you are trying to impress visitors; the occasional crisis. It was, however, a half-hearted effort at reassurance.

Full of roast pork and wine and punch-drunk from the conversation around me at lunch, I reflected that the phrase 'also-ran'

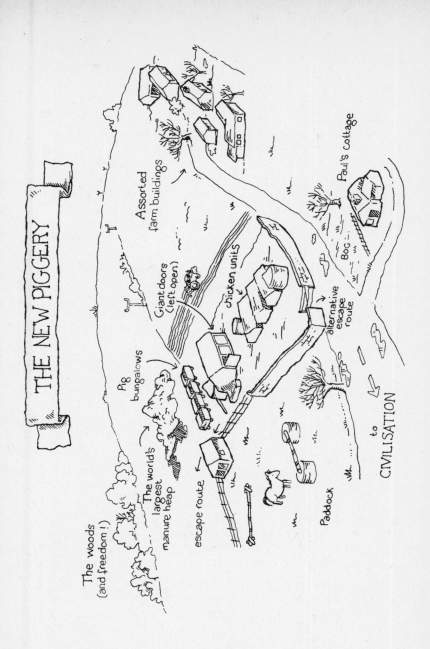

THE NEW PIGGERY

The woods
(and freedom!)

The world's
largest
manure heap

Pig
bungalows

escape route

Assorted
farm buildings

Giant doors
(left open)

chicken units

alternative
escape route

Paul's cottage

Bog

Paddock

to
CIVILISATION

125

was altogether too complimentary a term for my career in pigs. I really much more resembled one of those racehorses which not only crashes prematurely through the starting tape, but then unseats its jockey at the first fence, only to continue riderless – with my money on its back – all around the course, swerving round the fences and impeding all the other runners in turn, and wearing a stupid grin as it gallops past the stand to ironic applause. (Little did I realise that, encouraged by those who should have known better, I was later to own a very modest share in just such an animal.) I was not helped by my neighbour who, in reply to my complaint that my bank manager had threatened to increase my bank charges, remarked, '*I never borrow any money!*'

To cheer myself up I went and had a coffee with my old friend John Elliot who has always regarded my pig enterprises with some amusement. He made me feel appreciated by presenting me with a pocket calculator so slim that I suspected its purpose, but he assured me it had no sinister meaning and said, 'I've been keeping this especially for you.' I was able to talk to him quite knowledgeably about his breeding stock, because of a recent briefing by my Suffolk partner, Derek, who uses this stock. Aristocratic examples lay in pens, whiter than white, cocooned in fresh straw, in their abandoned poses looking like porcine Page Three models – and quite as attractive as some.

Refreshed and with some of my self-confidence regained, I joined Paul who was looking pensively at new piglet bungalows. (We had just invested in two second-hand ones, well into their dotage.) We decided it was time to call it a day and to head for home and Young Billaiki. On the way we stopped for a cup of tea and were joined by another farmer also on his way home from the Pig Fair. He did nothing to remove our feelings of inadequacy by talking cheerfully of starting up in pigs again. 'After all,' he said, 'I've already got all the buildings and equipment. The only costs will be for pigs and food.' How could we compete with such affluence?

But while we bumbled along at The New Piggery, finding even modest performance targets well beyond our reach, I did receive some consolation on my next visit to partners Derek and Gordon in Suffolk who had restocked after their Aujeszky's slaughter. Since their restocking with high-health pigs, they too had become so health conscious that I was subjected to a strip-search, reclothed, and sprayed with a pressure pump before I was allowed near their pigs, and then hurried through as though I had the plague. (Quite right too!)

So more often than not we now adopted the more comfortable habit of meeting in a local eatery, where we put our own world (and later, that of everyone else), to rights. The difference between their enterprise and that of The New Piggery was emphasised when Derek modestly produced his own latest costing results, which showed him to be top of his particular league. I was so impressed that I actually paid for the meal, and then wondered if I could claim it as 'management expenses'. Towards the bottom of the list were producers who had the sort of results which more nearly approximated to those of The New Piggery. On the selfish principle that there is nothing more encouraging than to see your neighbour in an even worse pickle than you are yourself, I returned home quite cheerfully.

There I was greeted by the sight of a very sweaty, very dirty and very harassed Paul trying to pull a very large, very dead sow out of her farrowing crate, where she had had the temerity to turn up her trotters just two days before she was to produce those 10.86 piglets to put us on the road to fame. (Peritonitis. Nine pigs, all dead.) It was just this sort of disaster which, however hard Paul tried, kept us firmly among the also-rans in the Porcine Championship Stakes. I had to change quickly into overalls, wellies and rubber gloves, for I find the smell of dead pig lingers for days, and lend a hand. It was obviously impossible for Paul by himself to pull getting on for 150 kilogrammes of stiffening sow out of her farrowing crate into the narrow passage, then to swing her round and drag her through the ex-Brummie front door. There is nothing more dispiriting than to consign to the knacker's yard an animal on the verge of repaying her board and lodging.

Such practical assistance on my part, especially in the later years at The New Piggery, was fairly rare. Indeed, even in his most generous mood, I doubt if Paul would have considered me a particularly energetic 'working' partner. My son William, with a certain amount of malicious glee, took to informing his cronies in the local market, hostelries and other places inhabited

127

by farmers of a sociable turn that 'Dad, of course, has virtually retired.' This intelligence was relayed back to me by one of my near neighbours, who found me cutting the lawn which, with our farmhouses now often worth more than our farms, I consider a fairly productive activity.

While I would have confessed in private to a certain indolence and lack of that dynamic drive so typical of thrusting youth, brought on by tempus fugiting and the superior claims on my time of watching slow horses and slower cricketers, I still considered that I did my share. This seemed at times to consist of trying to make sense of the accounts of three small enterprises, with three persons of varying moral rectitude manipulating the purse strings.

However, as in the above incident, there were still occasions when I entered the actual arena. I would pull on the sole remaining pair of punctured wellies and don the only suit of overalls left in the shed. This garment bore all-too-obvious signs of many too-intimate contacts with pigs some time previously, and of having fought losing battles with a number of sharp objects. So that when I eventually managed to find and to pull up the zip, I was festooned in a thing of rags and tatters, and I entered the yard to ribald and derisory comment.

One of these special occasions at The New Piggery was on a Sunday morning, the only time of the week when we had temporary help on the farm for such vital jobs as sorting out pigs, cleaning the cars, cutting the lawn and drinking my tea. The last-named activity always seemed to occupy an inordinate amount of time, and was far and away the most popular. On this particular Sunday we had on parade four lads, John, Darryl, Terry, and last but not least, Gareth. This was a full turn-out of the youngsters being groomed for stardom by son William. I suspect they regarded me as an old fogey. Together, these four were an exuberant quartet which, draped on my patio, rather resembled an out-of-work pop group. By himself, Gareth showed considerable promise as a comedian. He told me risqué stories, garnered from his comprehensive school, at which I tried to look shocked. The others laughed uproariously, and egged him on. Absent from parade were Paul, trying to pacify his wife by taking a few hours off to paper the bedroom, and William, on pleasure bent.

128

I and the boys were left to sort out a number of pigs ready to go for slaughter the following day, considered a simple enough task with which to entrust me. I firmly drew the line at officiating at such complicated procedures as weaning and weighing piglets (for one thing I could not stand the high-pitched squealing), or seeing to the mating of sows. There were just two snags. We had folk coming for lunch, so I was in a hurry; and we had just swept the whole yard in preparation for an inspection by the judges of a 'best-kept' farm competition, which in our arrogance we had foolishly entered. (We came second – out of two. But it was not so foolish; we won forty pounds!)

It was therefore important that we made as little mess as possible which, knowing the capacity of our pigs for creating mayhem out of the simplest operation, was likely to prove difficult. All hands were required to confine the piggy movements – not to mention their own movements – to as small an area as practicable. On my own I started preparations, all the lads still enjoying their mid-morning tea break, and a description of a day's beating at a pheasant shoot from Darryl, who aspired to be a gamekeeper. After a while I became impatient, and a great shout mustered two of them. These two then went in search of the other two, and I was on my own again. They found one, then disappeared again looking for the fourth. He slid out of the meal shed looking sheepish as soon as they had gone. Frenzied yells brought all the gang together at last.

Our first task was to select visually and mark the biggest pigs in the group. I had long ago given up weighing pigs (though Paul liked to do it), considering the stress and the aggravation to both man and beast not worth any gain in accuracy. Nor in my experience did the slaughterhouse returns bear much correlation to the individual liveweights of an on-farm weighing. I was sure that the regular pig-weighing Sunday session in which I used to partake shortened my life-expectancy considerably, though it provided much mirth to my assistants.

The selected pigs had then to be sorted out from the rest and driven out of their small outside yard over the pristine-clean concrete to the loading bay, where they could be penned overnight. Fronting their pen was one of our self-feeders. These are clumsy brutes at the best of times, and, as always seems to be the case on this sort of occasion, this one was full of food, extremely heavy, and even more awkward to move than usual. With a united effort and a 'one, two, three, heave' we pulled it open. Johnny and I went into the pen, carrying our patent pig-boards, wading through the sloshy dung at the front. We quite quickly sorted out fifteen candidates for the chop, and with the aid of our boards separated them from their pen-mates. The other lads successfully shepherded them over the concrete and into the loading bay.

So far so good. But then as so often happens, the boys rested on their laurels, relaxed, leaned casually on the barriers I had so carefully erected, and started to chatter about Boy George, the flavour of the month. Meanwhile, Johnny and I were having difficulty restraining the pigs left in the pen, who were anxious to join their mates. The selected pigs were in turn attempting to return to the pen from the alleyway to the loading ramp. If the two lots got together again, chaos threatened.

A yell from me brought the gossipers to heel. With one accord they leapt to attention, consigned Boy George to oblivion, shame-facedly grabbed hold of their boards, and came to our assistance. To set them a good example of what they should have been concentrating upon (always a dangerous ambition) I prepared to move the feeder back across the pen front, and relieve Johnny, who threatened to be overwhelmed by excited pigs. With a great tug I attempted to move the stubborn thing, it snagged on uneven concrete, I felt a sharp snap in my right calf, and with a shriek of pain I doubled up in agony. The four lads at first doubled up in mirth, then realised that it was not, for me at least, a laughing matter, and had the grace to look concerned. 'Are you all right?' asked Johnny, turning away to hide a grin and a look which almost said, 'Serves the old fool right.'

'No, I'm *not* all right,' I replied, my leg throbbing painfully.

Sweaty, dirty, and furious, I hobbled into the house, convinced I had broken a leg at least. It was, after all, just such a crack as I had heard several times on the rugger field. But my physio wife diagnosed a pulled muscle, slapped on an ice-pack – her great cure-all – pushed the (lunch) joint to one side, and whipped me off for further medical care and attention.

As we were leaving the yard, William, showered and smart,

130

came over to see what all the fuss was about. Bravely, I told him. 'But why didn't you let the boys move the feeder?' he asked, rubbing salt in the wound. If the boys had heard my answer they would have slunk home without even waiting for their next cup of tea.

Unfortunately, Paul and I were not to know when we decided to build The New Piggery from scratch that we were just entering a disaster area for pig farming. We suffered more than most, especially as we had high borrowings and insufficient turnover to service them. After several years of work and worry, hot on the heels of a quotation from our merchant of £128 a tonne for barley, which he cheerfully told Paul they were carting out of intervention stores to the docks to be transported to Spain at a cost to that country of £70 a tonne, came the news from our accountant that the last year had shown us an unhealthy loss.

Our resultant gloom was not helped by the action (sorry, inaction) of our water workers, who out of the kindness of their selfish hearts deprived us of mains water for all of four days. This meant that Paul and son William spent nearly every minute from five in the morning to eleven at night carting water from the nearest standpipe, all of three miles away, because the strikers refused to repair a broken water main near the farm. When we did eventually get our supply back, needless to say, late at night, ironically we very nearly suffered a flood, as many of the ball-valves got choked with grit and stuck open. Only Paul and William's alertness and all-night vigil prevented yet another disaster.

As the water workers were already earning far more than either Paul or William could hope for – especially after the news from our accountant – there was generated by them a head of steam about the merits of the water worker's case which was hot enough to boil a reservoir of their precious commodity. Preferably with the strikers in it! I was away in darkest Wales, where water gurgles from every nook and cranny. When I offered to return I was curtly told to stay where I was; that it was bad enough coping with the demands of the animals, without having me dipping my metaphorical oar in the murky depths of the dispute – not to mention flushing the toilet. Just as well I did stay put, for when I did get back I found that William

131

had had to drive a tractor over my beloved lawn to get to an old farm well.

I was greeted by a graphic flow-by-flow account of the emergency, and some pertinent remarks.

'Why,' asked Paul, 'did we hear nothing at all from all those so-called animal welfarists? They would have been on our backs like a ton of bricks if we let our animals go without water for a day, let alone four.'

'It must have cost us hundreds of pounds,' grumbled William, who thinks financially. I mournfully prodded the scars on my lawn.

Because of such setbacks, our optimistic expansion programme went along by fits and starts; that is, the bank manager had a fit and we made a start. Apart from money, finding the time was the biggest headache, for Paul was also managing the chicken unit to give him some income, and had little opportunity for DIY work. We could not afford to employ a regular worker, which is what we really needed.

When the Youth Training Scheme (YTS) started, we did employ one of these youngsters for a year. Sadly, he proved to be the sort of lad who needed constant supervision, and who was really rather more trouble than he was worth. Certainly not the type of worker whom Paul could leave to get on with even the routine work and know it would be done satisfactorily. Although he was a pleasant enough lad, he drifted around in an eternal dream-world, one of those Walkmans plugged into his ear blasting continuous pop music through his cranium, which prevented him from hearing what you said to him until he turned it off, or, for that matter, hearing what was going on around the unit. He was effectively insulated from all those different warning noises which tell you something is going wrong, though I doubt if he would have recognised the signals if he had heard them. He was also dreadfully slow. It took him so long to feed the pigs that it was almost time to start again before he had finished. Paul would return from his breakfast, and would be able to hear from the lane that some of his stock were still waiting to be fed. Enraged, he would track down our YTS to find him leaning on the front of a sow stall, food trolley beside him still full of grub, a sublime smile on his face, Walkman on his head, and eyes half closed. 'Whatever are you doing?' Paul

would ask in a shout. The YTS would come to earth with a
start, fiddle with his radio, and reply, 'Oh, I was just looking at
the pigs.' We never did find out whether this was just a weak
excuse, or whether he actually did have an irresistible urge to
commune with the pigs. He certainly spent every lunch hour
sitting on a bale in the farrowing house, though I suspect it was
because it was warm and cosy in there.

Like most teenagers he was happier on the tractor, and
whizzed around on this to some purpose – usually destructive –
as he swung the attached foreloader through a dangerous arc.
Paul did allow him to do some tractor work, but it was really
out of kindness, as we hardly dared leave him on his own in case
he went to sleep at the wheel, and we always had to clear up
behind him. Paul, who is nicer and more patient than me,
persevered with him for the whole year, but it was an exercise in
futility. He was a frail youth and we felt sorry for him and tried
to jolly him along. But like so many non-achievers from our
educational system, he seemed quite content just to mark time
through life, indifferent, even unaware, of any need to contribute.

Luckily, Paul had a motley and loyal gang of friends and
relations, many of whom were prepared to lend a hand at The
New Piggery for the sake of their livers or their lungs or their
hearts or, in extreme cases, all three. Fresh air and exercise was,
we told them, good for them, though by the look on the faces of
the joggers as they toil up our lane on their daily fix, I think this
is open to doubt. But most of these semi-willing volunteers had

133

other jobs and/or occupations to attend to, and were often not available just when we needed them most, particularly to help with further concreting. It seemed that Russell had disappeared into the snows for good and we could no longer rely on him to help us out. This was a pity, as the siting of the two prefabs, plus four piglet bungalows near them, had given us another large area to hardcore and concrete.

We had acquired these bungalows, which we badly needed to house our weaned piglets, from yet another ex-pig-keeper. He looked suspiciously at Paul when he arrived to collect the first of them, and then asked, 'Aren't you that chap whose photo was in the magazine last month?' Paul coyly admitted that it was indeed he who was posed with the sow (the star of the show) in an advertisement for worm pellets. 'Huh!' said the seller, 'Thought only models did that sort of thing.' Paul, who was really rather proud of his one claim to fame in the pig world, felt suitably deflated. As if he had not enough to do erecting and concreting around these piglet bungalows as well as all the other work, Paul had also ambitiously undertaken to build a large extension to his own bungalow. This scheme, not surprisingly, was such a time coming to completion that Paul's long-suffering wife became conditioned to living surrounded by builder's rubble. Even with a double armful of shopping she would step quite surely over ever-open trenches to reach her front door. She frequently found herself supplying board and lodging to those of Paul's friends whom he could persuade to spend a weekend in his company and that of a concrete mixer.

One of these assistants down for a therapeutic weekend was yet another lively character from Paul's rather eccentric college set. This chap, after any number of vicissitudes, had finally fetched up in the police force. He possessed the unenviable knack of doing the wrong thing at the wrong time. Shortly after joining the force he had managed to crash not one, but two, police cars, and to face prosecution for driving without due care, and then to crown his probation by booking his own sergeant for illegal parking. He was an enthusiastic if rather wayward helper, the sort of person to shovel ballast into the mixer with great panache, only to neglect to add any cement. He and Paul once spent several fruitless hours trying to pump water from flooded trenches, to discover later that the water was merely flowing back into the septic tank, and out again into the nearest trench.

The hardcore that Paul had been carting was a material called 'ash'. It is made, I think, from domestic refuse, and is quite splendid stuff, which spreads easily, sets hard, and is relatively cheap. The main snag from our point of view was that it had to be collected from an urban depot some miles away, where it was loaded by a large mechanical scoop. This machine was obviously conditioned to loading equally large and sturdy vehicles. The first time Paul went shyly in to pick up a load with our geriatic Fordson and small metal trailer the operator of this scoop picked up a massive bucketful, and from a height dumped it on to Paul's trailer. This poor thing gave an audible groan, the tyres bulged, and the front of the tractor nearly left the ground. The loader imperiously waved him on, and Paul was left to navigate this overload home.

As it proved difficult to restrain the enthusiasm of this autocratic loader, for we all know how power corrupts, much the same thing happened on subsequent visits. Even for someone with such a genial disposition as Paul, the journey home through busy suburban streets lowered the odds of him completing the hypertension marathon to about even money. On one such worrying occasion, one of the trailer tyres declared loudly that it had had enough, and collapsed with a loud sigh as Paul turned out of the High Street. As those of my readers who have experienced the trauma of being marooned in a sea of traffic with a broken-down vehicle, most parts of which could be held to contravene one or other traffic law, will be only too aware, this was real panic stations. Fortunately, Paul was not that far from his mother's phone. He manoeuvred his tractor and trailer as near to the kerb as he could, and sprinted up the road like a man possessed. Even more fortunately, he managed to contact son William first time.

William collected jack and wheel-brace, and drove to the scene, where Paul was chatting with a group of schoolchildren and directing the traffic. The jack was not man enough to lift the great dead weight of our load, and William had to go and borrow a stronger tool from a friendly garage. Then neither he nor Paul could shift the wheel nuts, which had been on since time immemorial, and he had to go off again in search of an extension lever and penetrating oil. Finally, with much grunting and grating of rust the nuts gave up their stranglehold without actually sheering, and the wheel was off.

It was quite obvious the tyre was a write-off. On the phone again. No, the local stockist did not have *that* size in stock. 'In fact, mate,' he said, 'I don't think they even make that size any more.' Back to the farm. One of our older trailers looked as though it might have a matching wheel. A repeat performance to remove this wheel, and back to the breakdown. An articulated lorry was just, only just, squeezing by. The driver leaned out of his cab and made a remark which fortunately we did not catch. It certainly did not look friendly. A police car drove by, stopped and reversed. Heart-stopping palpitations of all parties. 'Having trouble?' a kindly voice said. 'Be as quick as you can. Be rush hour soon.' Oh, blessed fuzz. It would also be dark soon, which would be even more serious for obvious reasons.

Joy of joy, the hubs matched, though the wheel itself was larger in diameter. It was on in a trice. Not a lot of air in it, as we realised when we lowered the jack; but surely enough to get us to sanctuary. Lopsided, one tyre scraping the floor of the trailer, we limped away from the houses and the traffic and a small knot of spectators who raised a parting cheer, into our friendly little lane. Back home at long last our faithful Fordson decided to throw a tantrum and refused to raise the trailer to tip the offending load. By now, we had ceased caring.

A year or so later we had an even more traumatic experience in rather similar circumstances in this same local town, which threatened to put all our other misadventures in the shade (of a cloud of smoke). We were fortunate enough to have an excellent free supply of wood shavings from a joinery works in a smoke-free zone, where producers have to pay to dump them. These were usually delivered to us in two large wooden boxes, which were surprisingly heavy, by the firm's lorry. There was always competition between Paul and William as to whether this useful litter should be for the pigs or the cattle, for both of them much preferred shavings to straw. 'Who's going to have them this time?' the driver would ask when he arrived very early in the morning. They usually finished up having a box each. The routine was that he would unload first, and then have breakfast with whoever received the second box.

But occasionally, we would receive an SOS from the firm. Either their lorry had broken down, or it was away on deliveries, and the boxes were full up and there was nowhere for the shavings being constantly manufactured to be stored. 'Can you do us a favour and come and get one of the boxes?' we would be asked. We did not like doing this, because we had to use a tractor and trailer on which the load was not particularly secure; we dreaded driving through the town with it; and we rarely had spare time or a spare driver. However, when they were desperate it seemed churlish to refuse.

On one such occasion Johnny was working on the farm. We last met Johnny helping me to sort out pigs. He had proved an excellent part-timer, keen and able; one of those lads you know will be good as soon as you see him walk about the farmyard with quick, purposeful strides. He came to us regularly one day a week, on a Thursday. So much has happened on this particular day that we have named it 'Black Thursday'. Poor Johnny always seemed to have to help us cope with some emergency, and he often threatened to change his day to one with more propitious omens. On one such Thursday William asked him to go and get a box of shavings, and he went off to the factory to be loaded. All went well until on the return journey, as he was negotiating a roundabout in the middle of the town, he suddenly heard a loud crack. A startled glance behind showed him that the drawbar had become free-moving rather than fixed. Slowly and carefully Johnny managed to ease the outfit up a small road to a private housing estate, away from the traffic. There he unhitched, left the trailer, and came back to the farm on the tractor to get assistance.

The situation was complicated. Working repairs on the spot did not appear practicable, so we had to transfer the heavy box from one trailer to another. William chased back to our ever-helpful neighbour and got him to come down with his fore-loader with forklift attachment. Unfortunately the forks were not long enough to get under the box to lift it. But he did manage with the aid of a rope to raise the box just enough for the trailer to be driven from under, and then lower it to the ground. Every time he tried to lift it onto the other trailer the box threatened to fall over. So William then went round to the joinery firm and by dint of forceful persuasion got them to agree to send their own

137

forklift. This William escorted through the town with warning lights flashing to the scene of the breakdown.

Meanwhile, the residents of the exclusive housing estate were beginning to agitate. 'When are you going to get that thing moved?' demanded one irate person, seemingly unaware of all the frenzied activity going on to do just that. Curtains twitched and eyes peered. Nobody offered to help.

Then William arrived with the forklift. This had no sooner pushed its prongs under the box preparatory to raising it, when its engine, overheated by the long trek through the streets, and covered in sawdust, caught fire. The driver yelled and jumped off. William rushed to the nearest house, banged on the door, and when it was answered by a woman asked, 'Can I have a bucket of water please, quick?'

'No you can't!' was the reply, and she slammed the door. It seems unbelievable, but it is true. Poor William! He is still convinced that if he had got a bucket of water then he could have quelled the fire immediately.

Another woman with two children in tow crossed the road to where the forklift was burning merrily away and threatening a minor, if not a major, conflagration. 'Can you ring the fire-brigade,' pleaded William. She regarded him with amazement, turned to Johnny and said, 'Is he serious?' (Johnny also swears this is true.) Luckily, a less sceptical person did summon the brigade, but with these delays the fire had got a good hold and had nearly destroyed the forklift before the brigade arrived, a very creditable few minutes after being called. A more public-spirited resident (or perhaps he just feared for his own property) had managed to rig up a length of hose from his kitchen tap to provide a small jet of water, and this William had kept spraying on the box to prevent that going up in flames too.

On the heels of the fire brigade came the police. 'My, you are in trouble,' said one police officer unnecessarily.

'Anyone hurt?' asked the other.

'No,' replied William through scorched lips, mentally adding that there might well be if he could get his hands on her. Before they drove off to their tea the policemen hung around for a few minutes, exchanging pleasantries with the on-lookers and chatting to the fire officers, who had been a model of helpful co-operation. ('We won't have to pay for their turnout, will we?'

138

asked a worried William of me when he eventually got home, blackened and tired.)

Meanwhile, Simon, the mechanic who does our repairs, had fortuitously arrived at the farm. I despatched him to help with the rescue. Strangely enough, he drove round the town a couple of times before he located the battleground, though to the combatants it felt as if the scene must be visible from London twenty miles away. I skulked in my house, only issuing out when I heard a tractor arrive, to get the latest bulletin from the front.

To complete William's discomfiture, the reinforced gang now managed to load the box onto the other trailer by using the first fore-loader and a combination of ropes and bodies to hold the box upright. It could have been very nasty if it had over-balanced onto the thrusting men. Squashed bodies on the pavement really would have given the residents something to complain about! Moreover, mechanic Simon also managed to repair the original trailer on the spot – it was a matter of broken weld and sheered bolts. Eventually, tractors, trailers, box and all were driven from the scene of action. The burnt-out forklift was collected by a breakdown, and, apart from ash and water, the street returned to its maidenly and private calm.

Some time later, when I had pieced together the details of the action from the garbled and (by now) amused recollections of the survivors, I rather unkindly remarked to son William, the general in command of operations, 'You got it all wrong didn't you?'

'I'm afraid so,' he admitted.

'I've never seen him look so worried,' said Johnny, with a broad grin. In truth, whatever the strategic mistakes, I was proud of all of them for their conduct under fire for the first time.

We also had another useful and money-saving arrangement. This was with a firm of ready-mix concrete suppliers, to take any material from them which had been left over or rejected – usually because all the men on a site had gone home – at a substantial discount. (The mind boggles at what might have happened if we had ever been asked to fetch *this* material!) This meant that we had to have a strip of ground always ready. It also meant that when we did have an area carefully prepared

139

we did not receive a delivery for months, and that when we had not, two lorries arrived just as we were off to the pub, and all our potential helpers were out or watching *EastEnders*.

Exactly this happened early one evening. The phone fetched me from my pre-prandial-drink shower, as the firm had been unable to contact Paul. Two lorries were on their way. As I adjusted my towel and put the phone down I heard them arriving. They were escorted by the car of one of the managers, to collect the money and to keep an eye on things. (There is, apparently, quite 'a grey area' surrounding the disposal of surplus goods such as this.) Dressed, I led them to the site where we had half-prepared an area for concreting, which Paul had unfortunately been using as a dumping ground for empty sacks, broken water bowls, and other flotsam and jetsam. Frenziedly, for drivers hate diverted journeys which keep them from their teas, I started to clear all this junk, and to search for suitable wood for shuttering, the meanwhile trying to placate the manager and promising the drivers 'a drink' if they hung around for a bit. Half-heartedly, they made a show of helping.

Just as the oppressiveness in the atmosphere was beginning to get me down, Paul and William arrived back from a trip to collect another second-hand piglet bungalow. This relieved the tension a little. It was important for us not to lose the opportunity for such loads. We soon cleared a sufficient area for one of the lorries to tip his load. This he did by cascading it down his swinging shute like a tidal wave, while we frantically tried to level it off before it engulfed us, and to rescue the lumps of hardcore thrown to the surface by the force of the delivery.

By now it was getting dark and cold, and William disappeared to find a large lamp carelessly left behind after a Young Farmers' barbecue and knees-up. Attached to the nearest prefab this threw some light on our operations, but also cast a lot of shadows and made accurate levelling difficult, working under pressure as we were. Pausing to wipe the sweat from my face, I suddenly recalled the occasion when I was at Twickenham watching the finals of the Middlesex Sevens, when a message came over the loudspeaker for a man up from Guildford. 'Your wife has just phoned. Will you please go home immediately as a lorry has just dumped a load of ready-mix concrete in your driveway and it needs levelling.' I told this to the others. Only

Paul laughed. Inspired, the second lorry, which had been churning around for what seemed like hours, spewed out his load with similar velocity to the first, and roared off into the darkness. As the manager also left, refusing my offer of a drink and clasping our cheque as though it was made of rubber, we assured him that we would be better prepared next time, and would welcome such loads in the future. He did not look either convinced or enthusiastic.

We were left with an undulating mass of wet concrete, and we were not helped when the lamp blew at the same time as part of the makeshift shuttering sagged outwards into the gloom. At this I opted out, and left Paul and William to finish off under the flickering light of two torches held by Paul's long-suffering wife, who had come to see what all the fuss was about, and to tell Paul that his supper was ready.

Next morning came the day of reckoning. In the cold light of day we realised that we now had an area of new concrete varying from four to twelve inches thick, much of it laid on a quivering base, with puddles of water from overnight rain in the low places, and clear imprints from the feet of my dog, Paul's moggie, and a marauding fox. In one place a long frond of unidentifiable weed was trapped in the concrete, which may give future archaeologists food for thought, as they excavate for evidence of the existence of an extinct species, the twentieth-century livestock farmer. Still, the concrete survived, and was a lot better than mud.

Whatever future archaeologists may think, in the present Paul and I were certainly being given food for thought as we reflected on the dramas and traumas of our time together. As I sat over my muesli and toast one morning – for only young bloods like Paul and William now dare the traditional and satisfying fry-up – I was brought up short by a sentence in a farming article. 'I recall,' it read, 'several instances where farmers starting new herds did not plan for all the little things that do go wrong.' Oh dear, oh dear! Paul and I appeared not only to have neglected to do that, but also to make allowances for the big things that go wrong as well. To give just one example, our carefully designed fattening house, based upon the principles of deep litter, self-feeding, and easy cleaning-out (surely all admirable ideas?), had been universally condemned

141

by any expert to whom we were brave enough to show it. Meanwhile, we were lumbered with it. And as confessed in this saga, most of our other plans, such as that to start at The New Piggery with new stock from one source, had gone equally awry. I was humbled to realise that my Suffolk partners had made a much better go of their restocking, but then they rightly regard most of my ideas as unworthy of serious consideration.

However, as some consolation, later in the same article the writer did admit to losing four sows in a heat-wave. Now, we had lost sows by almost every other way devised by man, beast and the Almighty, but never, as yet, through heat. But then, the writer ran an outdoor system, and we did not, and I was full of admiration for anybody who not only could, but did, rear pigs outside.

For many stressful, usually nocturnal, occasions spent rounding up straying cattle, sheep, and, yes, pigs too, early in my chequered farming career convinced me that the only way for me to keep animals, if I wished to enjoy my self-employed pension, was securely under lock and key. One of my few experiences of sows kept outside was many years ago when on a visit to those Suffolk partners I foolishly offered to help feed the sows, which were in a small field because we had no buildings.

As I carried two buckets of wet grub through the gooey mud my legs and my wellies parted company, and my next involuntary step into the mire saturated my socks and my lower trousers. I put down the buckets, which instantly fell over, and half-turned to pull out my wellies, which came out with a nasty sucking sound. Clasping these muddy objects in my hands I aimed a bad-tempered kick at two inquisitive sows who had sloshed up to investigate and were slurping up the spilled meal. My remaining leg stuck fast in the mud and, off-balance, I fell over. The plumbing arrangements in Derek's house at that time did not allow for a vast consumption of hot water, and it took me some time to clean up. Even then, I drove home direct, not daring to stop in even the dingiest, most out-of-the-way pub for a soothing draught.

Chapter Thirteen

'Oh don't bother me!' said the Duchess. 'I never could abide figures!'
(L. Carroll)

I IMAGINE THAT, rather like public schools, prisons, the MCC and other confined and exclusive establishments, each pig unit develops a collective personality of its own. Certainly the ones I have been associated with do.

At The Piggery, for instance, the inmates were not only accident prone, but were also determined to catch every known disease, plus a few which they invented for themselves. At times their health status approximated to that of the citizens of London during the Great Plague, and half the pens should have had a red cross on their doors, with, as Pepys wrote, 'and "Lord have mercy on us" writ there.'

On my own farm, the pigs I imported from Suffolk were rather too obviously 'gay', had never heard of AIDS, and spent

all the time not occupied in eating and sleeping, behaving in a quite unmentionable fashion. That is, when they were not scrapping. Their embarrassing antics, like those of exhibitionist monkeys at the zoo, should have provoked a coyly averted glance and brought a blush to the cheeks of visitors, but, alas, we are all case-hardened these days. Even children no longer ask, 'What *are* they doing?'

At The New Piggery we bred a species of escape artist, the father founder being the hurdling boar. He could clear a four-foot barrier without effort, and sadly – for it might have quietened him down a bit – without touching it with any part of his anatomy. He was, you will recall, a runaway winner of the Porcine Champion Hurdle, but was disqualified the following year for not keeping his mind on the job. In our early days at The New Piggery we had few secure compounds once the inner defences were breached. Although Paul lectured his charges on the conventions attaching to an open-prison system, he was frequently greeted by sows wandering up the road towards him, or cavorting in and around the dung heap or the stored building materials and feedstuffs. The condition of none of these is improved by close acquaintance with inquisitive pigs.

As time passed we managed to erect an outer perimeter fence. This did help, unless the gate (as often happened) had been left open, or part of the fence had been demolished (as more often happened) by our YTS lad, who never seemed to realise that a tractor with a fore-loader attached is longer than a tractor by itself; nor that our concrete approach road was not the slip road from the pits at Brands Hatch. (To give him his due, his excuse that the brakes were uneven was true.) The border lighting outside The New Piggery and the chicken unit did not deter any escapees. It merely showed the way.

So it was no surprise when Paul one dark and chilly evening was phoned up by a never wildly co-operative neighbour who lived some two miles down the lane to be told that 'yer . . . pigs are out again Guv.' It was rather more surprising when the phone immediately rang again with a message from the pub two miles down the lane the other way that there were sows in their car park. Being more concerned to mollify the latter before the former, Paul quickly hitched on the trailer and sped off to the pub. There he was greeted by an excited and boisterous group of stag-night revellers, who appeared to have spotted not only any number of large pigs, but a number of pink elephants as well.

However, there was no sign of any pigs, though Big White Hunter Paul with his jungle-trained eye did spot evidence of their spoor. This he hastily and surreptitiously kicked under a new Jaguar, before the proud owner stepped in it. Donning his sola topi, he spent the next ten minutes cruising up and down the lane peering into the dark until he saw one errant sow grazing contentedly among the flowerbeds of a keen local gardener. Paul and his wife Nicky – who always, poor soul, found herself involved in these dramas – with as little noise as possible managed to corner the sow in the drive, and with the help of a bucketful of meal coax her into the trailer. Paul accelerated away just as lights flashed on in the hall of the house.

The escapee was no sooner unloaded and reunited with her mates, and Paul with his interrupted supper, when the phone rang again to ask why he had not been down to collect the sows from the other end of the lane. Paul, being uncertain of the exact number of sows which should have been in any one pen at any one time, once more abandoned his supper and took to the trail with his faithful Number Two. And yes, I know, in a well-managed unit this information would at the very least be chalked on the wall if not stored in the computer. But those who have followed the saga this far will recognise that good management was not our strong suit. Our unit was still in a state of organised chaos, with sows dossed down all over the place in varying states of dishabille, rather like the sleeping arrangements on the farm following one of those long-running teenage parties. To complicate matters, Paul had just weaned a number of sows, and the lights did not work in two of the sow yards.

A fruitless and hungry half-hour later, including a tense exchange of pleasantries with the neighbour who had telephoned and had assumed the sows were still around because his whippet had barked – 'that something dog will bark at its something shadow' remarked Paul – convinced him that just one athletic and adventurous miscreant was probably responsible for all his troubles. The next morning he spoke very severely to her, actually going so far as to boot her up the backside as she wandered wearily up to the trough. 'I was only looking for my piglets and got carried away,' her pained expression seemed to say, and Paul felt instant remorse.

The piglets were just as adept as their mums in getting out from any assumed secure enclosure. The pig bungalows we had purchased had the usual arrangement of covered sleeping area and an open slatted dunging area with water bowl. Well-ordered weaners popped through their bedroom hatch to drink, and to obey the rules of their potty training handbook. Most of ours were more catholic in their preferences. Even though the sides of the outside area were relatively high and vertical, somehow our newly weaned piglets, just five weeks old and not fancying life without Mum, managed to clamber up them and to fall over the edge into the slurry pit below with a nasty, sloshy thud. Miraculously, they would pick themselves up, give themselves a good shake, then scurry off as fast as their little legs would take them in search of Mother. Because of shortage of space she was usually temporarily housed in the loading bay, awaiting the amorous attentions of Dad. Her piglets would squeeze under the metal gate like Limbo dancers in a hurry, and Paul would arrive to find the piglets he had just laboriously weighed and weaned snuggled back under maternal protection. He would return these smelly miscreants to their proper quarters, only for them to find that they were now shunned by their mates, who cruelly pushed them out of the sleeping area into the cold. This made the rejected weaners even more determined to escape. Paul found that even a heavy temporary lid did not deter them. Somehow, someway, they managed to shove it up and squeeze out again. No wonder if I asked Paul, 'And how many weaners are there in this one?' he would answer doubtfully, 'Well, there *should* be 35.'

Paul had other statistical problems, besides keeping track of exact numbers. For, by now, our herd had expanded to quite a respectable size, and should have started to keep us rather than we keeping them, if only we could have persuaded them to rear more piglets to the kindergarten stage. The increase was mainly because we had purchased a job lot of sows from a friend. He had happily given up pigkeeping when he sold some of his land for building; a much more profitable use of resources and the dream of every landowner near an urban fringe. Unfortunately he had rather lost interest in what had been a good herd, and was unable to furnish Paul with an accurate list of farrowing and service dates.

So for the next few months Paul was continually being surprised by unexpected farrowings in the sow stalls, or by belated evidence that a sow had failed to hold service. Nor did this group settle at all happily in their new home where bugs, attendants, routine and accommodation were all different from their last cosy quarters. It was, I regret, yet another of our mistakes, once again the result of our anxiety to achieve a reasonable cash flow and a decent turnover to finance our bank borrowing, the spectre of which was beginning to loom over us rather like Dracula in the novitiate of a convent.

We had now been at The New Piggery for five momentous years but the precariousness of our future was brought home to us on our next annual pilgrimage to the office of our accountant. Here we were courteously informed, with our accountant's genius for understatement, that 'things don't look all that promising. I'm afraid you've made a small loss again this year.' The only consolation was that this loss was after drawings and (smiling) 'my fees'. He did some complicated calculations on his electronic computer – he is not that hot at mental arithmetic, I'm pleased to report – then announced, 'That's where it is. Sales of pigs.' We smiled wanly. We already knew that. If only one could survive without making profits how much more pleasant life would be; but only the nationalised industries appear to have achieved that sublime state. We were ushered from his carpeted, quietly lit sanctum into the cold, hard world outside, feeling that only divine intervention could solve our problems. And this led me to compose the following:

PARABLE

Here beginneth the last chapter in the epistle of Peter and Paul, disciples of St Porcine.

The following parable is told to encourage those among you who too have trodden that hard and stony path which inexorably leads to the desert of disillusion and disappointment, rather than to that promised land of milk and honey and excess profits. For the mote in a neighbour's eye can produce

147

a twinkle in one's own. And how heartening it is, dear brethren, to find other of the Gadarene swine in that craft being rowed by the awful Charon over the Styx to Penury.

Now it so happened that Peter and Paul, having delivered their inscribed tablets to a certain John, a follower of the heathen god Chartered Accountancy, went later to his temple to be told of their fate. And yea, this John disclosed unto them, with many a significant gesture, that their last twelve months of toil and trouble had yielded them not a morsel of comfort or recompense. Verily, their tablets when transcribed showed that they had sacrificed some seven thousand paper pounds on the altar of the stern and unforgiving God, Mammon.

This sacrifice was ordained at first to be but half that awful amount, until it transpired that a certain three thousand five hundred of those pounds, which had been spent on the purchase of loaves and fishes, had by a slip of the felt-tipped quill moved into the Wrong Column, where they had masqueraded as a Good Credit rather than a Bad Debit. Upon discovery, this gloomy intelligence was communicated by the said John with a jolly laugh, as though a mere three thousand five hundred pounds here or there was but a matter of small import and signifieth nothing. To the two disciples, this portentous revelation appeared as the Last Straw did to the benighted camel in Noah's Ark.

Peter and Paul regarded one another, and with true Christian fortitude and denial determined to look upon what is in the well-known Society of Optimistic Farming Asses (SOFA) called 'the bright side'. This vision of good cheer principally came from the smoke signals of such costings prophets as the Mighty Ridgeon from the arid plains of East Anglia, whose acolytes, to the immense satisfaction of Peter and Paul, also inhabited a 'loss situation'. Which, praise be to Allah, appeared to be at least as uncomfortable as that occupied by the said Peter and Paul.

The Mighty Ridgeon and his fellow prophets nevertheless held out hope for the future. As ordained by the God

148

Mammon, many of their followers had fallen by the wayside, so their goods would no longer compete in the market place with those of the survivors of the pilgrimage. But verily, many of those pilgrims still travelling the stony track to the ray of hope on the celestial horizon wore stronger apparel and carried better-filled packs than possessed by Peter and Paul.

Peter and Paul in their infinite wisdom deliberated upon the trials and tribulations of their last year. They had struggled to increase the number of vestal virgins in their St Porcine Chapel from fifty to seventy-five. This holy place was ill-equipped and had a leaky roof and draughty sides, but the congregration most obstinately refused to contribute through their reproductive activities to a building fund, being more concerned with the sins of gluttony and devious sexual pleasure. So that, as the prophet Catch Twenty-Two saith, without shekels it is difficult to improve, yet shekels were in short supply.

Also during that troubled year, upon advice from on high, Peter and Paul had invested such funds as they could rescue from the clutches of their adversaries into the purchase of Superior Stock, the better to reproduce the progeny of the St Porcine Chapel even unto the third and fourth generation; so that from the loins of these Superior Grandparents should spring a race to astonish the marketplace, give joy to the disciples, and gladden the hearts of the middlemen. To house the sacred progeny in their probationary stage, four humble dwellings denominated The Bungalows had been purchased and erected nigh the St Porcine Chapel. From these dormitories the sacrificial stock were moved through the portals of the mighty New Piggery, there to be prepared for the tables of the ungodly.

By faith, hope and (mainly) charity the ordained numbers had been achieved. Though the young and virtuous maidens in that enlarged herd were slow to mate, slower to conceive, and even slower to deliver, by the end of the sacred year in question their performance was beginning, as testified by the great and good MLC, to approach some

149

respectability. Indeed, in moments of sublime euphoria Peter and Paul elevated themselves from their humble origins into the ranks of the learned and blessed who proudly and worthily inhabit a Profit-Making Situation. But the kind and clever and good scribe from the great and good MLC informed them gently that this was but wishful thinking. 'You must first approach the steep heights of the Top Third,' she said, her pocket computer humming in her hands.

Peter and Paul, their caps held humbly in their hands, approached with some trepidation and quaking of limbs the mountain of Lloyds to give account of their adventuring. From the summit the revered hermit in his warm and luxurious cave (no sackcloth and ashes for the followers of the great God Usurer), met them with guarded friendship and understanding. He listened carefully to their tale of woe and to their prognostications of good omen, wrote with his gold-tipped quill mystic signs on his tablet, took a large grain of salt, yet spake words of encouragement and hope.

Yea, even more significant, the sacred overdraft was left unsullied. The sage wept tears of compassion and joy with his suitors that the holy indicator designated by the cognoscenti the AAPP (Average All Pigs Price) was rising up the graph. He merely tempered his homily by insisting that all and every one of those worldly possessions denominated 'assets' and which were secreted in the modest hovels of the said Peter and Paul be ascribed to the said Lloyds mountain, which hath great need for such security to maintain their temples and the dwellers therewith in sumptuous style. For from the contributions of the needy do such great institutions flourish.

And yet, O ye of little faith, Peter and Paul went down from the mountain refreshed. They joined hands in friendship and walked towards the golden dawn, merely pausing in a neighbouring hostelry to gather strength to control the unholy orgy of the vestal virgins which, O dear Lord, probably awaited them on their return to The New Piggery.

However, we had to take the sort of results we were achieving (or not achieving) seriously, and be realistic about the future. Seven years of sweat and toil had never yielded Paul a decent income, let alone given him the opportunity to accumulate any capital. The future for farming in general looked bleak. For the part of that industry producing that bête noire of the cholesterol-watching lobby, meat for human consumption, the future looked even bleaker. The EEC supported cereals excessively, pigmeat not at all. On the one hand we were buying artificially expensive feed, on the other selling in a very competitive, free market.

We discussed interminably the options open to us. By the end of the bottle we were even more confused as to what to do. Paul was, not unnaturally, most reluctant to give up, because, as he said, 'It seems that I have failed. And I don't want to let you down.' But we had to face the fact that the only organisation earning any real money out of The New Piggery was the bank, and our borrowings were getting out of hand. We had never recovered from the really bad years when everyone, not just us, lost money. To continue in any way as livestock producers would still require the borrowing of large sums of dear money. If we got out now, Paul would probably still have enough capital available to give him a deposit on a house.

In the end I said, 'Look Paul, see if you can get another job. If and when you do, we can then make our minds up.'

Paul completed an impressive-looking curriculum vitae, composed an explanatory letter about his more recent activities, and started sending off applications. He sent off over forty in reply to advertisements for jobs for which his chemical engineering and farming background might be appropriate. Paul was naturally keen to stay in a farming-related industry. There was no positive response, though he received an occasional tentative approach and had one or two interviews. Instead of retreating into a shell, losing heart and feeling unwanted, which many would have done, Paul took a fresh look at his method of applications. He revised his cv to give the minimum rather than the maximum of detail, made a précis of his covering letter, and launched off another batch to prospective employers. This proved a great success, for his qualifications and experience were obviously intriguing enough in general terms for

152

employers to want to know more about him, and he was called to a number of interviews.

I shared with him his frustration at this time. It was sad enough to be giving up our enterprise, without having to search in a very competitive field for a new occupation. However, his perseverance was finally rewarded, ironically enough, by the offer of not one, but two jobs. One of these was near enough for him to maintain local contacts, was connected with farming, had a starting salary of some ten thousand pounds, plus a new car. It also offered responsibility and prospects. 'You are never going to earn that in a month of Sundays running a pig unit,' I said, feeling a trifle envious. We both knew he would be foolish not to accept.

One of my enduring memories of Paul is the sight of his little van racing up our lane, leaving a great wave of spray in its wake as it splashed through the puddles. He was on his way from The Piggery to The New Piggery when he was commuting between both. Now for a time he commuted from his new office to help with the rundown of The New Piggery, but this time more sedately and in a smart company car. A thankfully competent YTS did the daily chores, weekends were devoted to weaning and sorting out the stock for sale.

Stubborn to the last, after a few months of clearing out and cleaning up, we were left with the real diehards. Squash-nosed, thin and mottle-fleshed, these pigs adamantly refused to fatten. None of us fancied them in the freezer. One by one we trickled them in with decent pigs to go to the abattoir where more often than not they got their final revenge by being totally condemned.

As we slammed the trailer ramp shut on the very last one, a car drove into the yard. A smart young lady, briefcase in hand, got out. 'I've come to see the wages book of The New Piggery,' she announced.

Gently, I explained that there were no employees and certainly no wages, and that the wages book was with Paul fifteen miles away.

'Come and have a cup of coffee instead,' I said.

Here endeth the final chapter from the epistle of Peter and Paul to St Porcine, the patron saint of cloven-hoofed quadrupeds — especially those which go well (when deceased) with apple sauce or grilled mushrooms.

Cloven-hoofed bipeds are best avoided. Like swine dysentery.

May the blessing of St Mammon be among you, now and (hopefully) for ever more.

Saying thus, Peter and Paul departed The New Piggery. And slipped down among the slurry.

FARMING PRESS

Farming Press publishes a wide list of books about farming.

On the humorous side there are books by Emil van Beest, Henry Brewis, James Robertson and John Terry, each of whom sees the funny side of agriculture in his own distinctive way.

The range of practical books for farmers and students published by Farming Press is unrivalled in Britain. The list includes titles on pig, sheep, dairy and arable farming as well as many other farming and veterinary topics. Farming Press also publishes three monthly magazines – *Arable Farming*, *Dairy Farmer* and *Pig Farming*. Much of the material included in *The Confessions of An Also-Ran* originally appeared as *Pig Farming* articles.

For a free illustrated catalogue of books or specimen magazines please contact:

Farming Press, Wharfedale Road, Ipswich IP1 4LG.